Understanding Alternative Medicine

Scripture text: The Holy Bible, New International Version.
Copyright © 1978 by New York International Bible Society. First
published in Great Britain 1978. Used by permission of New York
International Bible Society.

Life Changing Books
3 Beggarwood Lane, Basingstoke, Hants, RG23 7LP, UK
and
New Wine Press
PO Box 17, Chichester

Copyright © 1985 by Roy Livesey
First published by Bury House Christian Books in 1983 under the
title Beware Alternative Medicine

ISBN 0 551 01235 8
New Wine Press ISBN 0947852 08 5

Reproduced, printed and bound in Great Britain by
Hazell Watson & Viney Limited,
Member of the BPCC Group,
Aylesbury, Bucks

Contents

TO RAE – my patient wife who never entertained yoga and the like in her own life, but who was to watch my full-time involvement in 'alternative medicine'. She could not precisely put her finger on why it was abhorrent to her, but when at length fear came, God spoke to her. 'Trust Me', He said. She heard Him clearly and was at peace again.

DEDICATED TO THE GHS – *God's Health Service.* Jesus died to give us the GHS. Of course He uses human agents including those in the NHS. All is far from right with God in the NHS and the omission of more than the passing references in this book is recognised. *All* Satan's Secret Services have to be flushed out. God provides the necessary discernment for *all* medicine in the fellowship of Christians. This book makes a start by looking at 'alternative medicine'. The objective is God's Health Service with Satan excluded from man's medical activity.

The man without the Spirit does not accept the things that come from the Spirit of God for they are foolishness to him and he cannot understand them, because they are spiritually discerned. (1 Corinthians 2:14).

Acknowledge...

I thank my own Elim Christian
minster for its support as I
My thanks also go to fellow
Gospel Businessmen's Chapte
in a variety of ways. Thanks to
and others who have given va
various drafts. I am grateful t
supported me in prayer. Mo
sponded since reading the Fir
I have never met. I am grate
material I have received from
it has been incorporated in wh

For all those dear people, and m
least to my wife, Rae, and m
David, all in the front line w
the book has gone ahead.

sound therapies, hydrotherapy,
aromatherapy, macrobiotics, zone therapy,
orgonomy (Reichian therapy), bio-
energetics, do-in, Feldenkrais technique,
rolfing, mora therapy, orthobionomy

Preface by The Rt. Revd. Derek Rawcliffe*, Bishop of Glasgow and Galloway

I would like to commend the second edition of Roy Livesey's book, which is now entitled *Understanding Alternative Medicine*. He learned through painful personal experience that the realm of alternative medicine has been thoroughly invaded by Satan in the form of occult practices which at first sight can seem so innocent and even helpful, but which have a sting in their tail in some form of bondage to the evil one. The thing that pulled Roy Livesey up sharply and made him realise the origin of the forces he had been searching into was the ugly death of a fellow searcher after a week of torment at the hands of demonic spirits.

The purpose of this book is to alert Christians to the presence of the occult in some of the forms of alternative medicine which are coming more and more into vogue today and to give them the information which will enable them, with the guidance of the Holy Spirit, to judge whether a particular form of alternative treatment is from God or whether it is bound up with the occult, ie with Satan, and therefore forbidden to Christians. He is not therefore saying that all forms of alternative medicine are wrong but is giving us the data so that we can make right decisions and avoid accepting blindly some seem-

11

ingly innocent treatment which will eventually yield its crop of misery.

Some people, even Christians, will find it hard to believe that Satan has got his hands on so many forms of alternative medicine or has fostered so many deceptions. Roy Livesey knows that this is true from his own experience. I know it through ministering to people who have got themselves involved in the occult. I hope that Christians will heed the warning in this book and keep away from these false forms of healing, while fostering true healing in Jesus' name; and that those who are not Christians will also be led to keep away from those dangerous practices and put their faith in Jesus, God's only son.

These occult practices are not nonsense. They are real, they have power. But they are evil and dangerous. But I want to bear witness with Roy Livesey that Jesus Christ has won the victory over them through his death and resurrection and that we can share in that victory through repentance and faith in Him.

*Derek Rawcliffe spent most of his ministry in the South Pacific where he became the first Bishop of the New Hebrides in 1974. He later became Bishop of Glasgow and Galloway.

Foreword by Dr. Douglas Calcott,* LRCP, MRCS, MB, BS

One of the remarkable things about the Body of Christ on earth today is the uniform expectancy that our Lord's return is near. The day is near when we shall see Him as He is and we shall be like Him. He will appear as the Lord of Glory.

The truth, of course, is that He is just the same now. He is Lord of all. Peter's words in Acts 10:36 were 'Jesus Christ – He is Lord of all'. Jesus is the same yesterday, today and forever.

The Lord wants to have this supreme place in our lives now. In the wilderness God proved to the Israelites that He could give them food and water and save their shoes and clothes from wearing out. He would have done far more if they had let Him and not disobeyed His laws.

Our Lord wants to prove His sufficiency in every area of our lives today, especially in the area of health. He wants to reveal to us that He has dealt with sickness as well as sin on the cross. He is the greatest physician.

Satan is desperate to deceive us on this issue and has raised up many counterfeit physicians and methods of treatment.

Roy Livesey, in this unique book, is opening our eyes to Satan's deceptions. They look good and give results but come from the wrong source and the wrong power. As the doctor in the testimony Roy writes on homoeopathy, I can say that, since renouncing homoeopathy as occult, I have found my relationship with Jesus much more real and effective. I am seeing Him heal as I pray

13

against sickness in His name, something I had come to accept would never be my experience.

Homoeopathy, though producing results, had robbed me of faith in the highest source of healing: Jesus Christ the Son of God.

Roy has been very courageous in presenting the truth. Although this truth may offend some, I trust that for many it will be the truth that sets them free.

* Douglas Calcott is a medical practitioner who previously served in the Royal Army Medical Corps and then as an ophthalmologist in Kenya. He is active in evangelism, counselling and Bible teaching. Until renouncing homoeopathy as occult he was a member of the Faculty of Homoeopathy. He practised homoeopathy and he had studied the subject for nearly twenty years.

Introduction

I spent nearly twelve months as a full-time 'searcher' in the forbidden area of occult 'healing'. Prompted by terror and horrifying experiences, I was led by a long-standing clergyman friend to a Christian who had a particular understanding of the crisis point I had come to. He was the first really to get through to me with the consequences of my involvement in the innocent-sounding areas of 'healing' and 'alternative medicine'. That was my first introduction to the man who is now my pastor, Rev. Mick Reynolds.

Looking next at all the dangers, I was led to the idea that I must be born again and baptised by the Holy Spirit. I didn't understand what all that really meant but I wasted little time in getting to a service at the Elim Christian Fellowship in Kidderminster. Rev. George Miller, an evangelist, was ministering that night. Jesus Christ became real to me and I was baptised by the Holy Spirit.

Not long after that, God put it on my heart to do two things. I had to give my testimony to my old colleagues in 'alternative medicine'. I was able to tell them my life had been totally changed. A peace and satisfaction had come to me through knowing Jesus. Secondly, I had to expose Satan's counterfeit healing to all.

This then is a *warning* book. I do not pretend to have all the answers nor am I condemning all the alternative therapies mentioned in this book. Rather it is my purpose to encourage Christians to exercise their own caution, enquiry and discernment. The occult is on the increase but the Lord is revealing to His people the truth about various practices. The testimonies on homoe-opathy are examples.

Without discernment, Christians can be led into occult 'alternative medicine'. Sadder still, without knowledge of the evil in it, there can be no possibility for us to alert those who are blind and cannot see and to whom things of the Spirit appear as foolishness (1 Cor. 2:14).

The book does not pretend to be a work of great scholarship! Prayerfully written, it is none-the-less an urgent book. Taken from my own testimony, and from what scripture reveals, it is at least a book by one who has travelled the way of 'alternative medicine'.

The thief came seeking to steal and kill and destroy, but Jesus was there that I may have life, and have it to the full (John 10:10).

November, 1983

Second (Enlarged) Edition

Christians in Britain receive many warnings about *cults*, drawn from the vast experience in the United States. Since the first edition was written, I have travelled in the United States, listening, and speaking at many Christian meetings on the subject of alternative medicine. I believe the greatest experience of this phenomenon is to be found in the United Kingdom. The explosion in occult medi-cine has happened here. Unlike in America, under British common law anyone can set up as a therapist, provided only that he doesn't claim to be a medical doctor.

The Second Edition is much bigger than the first: over one hundred therapies are included, some harmless, but the great majority having a harmful spiritual basis. Yet I fear there may be insufficient here to satisfy one of the well-known reviewers of the First Edition: '. . . isn't it time that a group of Christians with the theological, scientific, professional and medical qualifications plus the gift of spiritual discernment, wrote an authoritative and weighty book on this subject?' Perish the thought!

I trust my Christian readers will find that, with God, things are really not so complicated. I believe they will find much here to help them exercise the discernment that God will give them.

A change has been made in the title for this Second Edition, and the significance of alternative medicine in the New Age is brought into focus. Perhaps inevitably, there will be the tendency to look for what is written about this or that therapy. However I believe an *understanding* of alternative medicine will be helped by reading steadily through the book. The context in the New Age, and in the expansion of interest in the occult realm, will be more clearly seen. I believe such an approach will be an aid to discernment on any particular treatment. The main purpose of the book is to encourage readers to strengthen their own discernment.

For such men are false apostles, deceitful workmen, masquerading as apostles of Christ. And no wonder, for Satan himself masquerades as an angel of light. (2 Corinthians 11:13–14)

How you read this book is very important

Satan and his work is revealed. He would seek to blind us against the truth of God's Word on occult 'alternative medicines' and false healers – Satan's counterfeits of God's true work of healing.
Jesus Christ paid for our freedom, and victory over Satan, with his life. So pause now, and pray that God will open your eyes to all the truth and that He will give you the help you need in order to act on what you know to be the truth.

Note. Whilst this book clearly identifies areas of so-called healing that are quite certainly occult it is emphasised that the main purpose is to encourage Christians to be discerning. Many names are mentioned in the course of showing the variety, and giving a picture, of the alternatives to what the doctor offers. However, just as orthodox medicine is not always free from the demonic, so 'alternative medicines' are not necessarily powered by the demonic. The mere mention of an 'alternative medicine' in this book is not to be taken as any suggestion that it is occult.

PART ONE
THERE ARE 'HEALERS' ABOUT!

Let no-one be found among you . . . who practises divination or sorcery . . . engages in witchcraft . . . or who is a medium or spiritist or who consults the dead. Anyone who does these things is detestable to the Lord (Deuteronomy 18:10–12).

Today's sorcerers, diviners, white witches and spiritists are busy 'healing'. It is only the names that are different. Satan has had a plan since Adam, and his demons are as busy now as they were then.

- **Whether** we look at the 5,000 year old 'secrets' like acupuncture, reflexology and meditation, **or**
- **whether** we look back only 500 years to Paracelsus, **or**
- **whether** we look back 150 years to his follower Hahnemann who gave us homoeopathy, **or**
- **whether** we look at the newest techniques or some of the therapies at new healing centres,

what we find is spiritual power rooted in the occult.

1: Some basic questions answered

Sickness comes from Satan

When we start to doubt God's Word, we are not the first. Adam and Eve, in perfect conditions, failed the test. Satan, the author of sin, sickness and death, acting through a serpent, tempted them to doubt God's Word. 'You can be like God', he told them. God had warned they would surely die if they took the fruit. It was Satan who caused them to sin. Sin and sickness go together. Jesus spent his time on earth dealing with both. At the cross he paid the price of our salvation with His blood, and the price of our healing with His wounds. *He himself bore our sins in his body on the tree, so that we might die to sins and live for righteousness; by his wounds you have been healed* (1 Peter 2:24).

True healing comes only from God: beware Satan's counterfeits!

Sickness comes from Satan and it isn't surprising that he also tries to take it away. Healing methods are more and more counterfeited by demons in these days. Satan's deceitful healings make things much worse. Spiritual power can come from only two sources:

1. Jesus
Jesus has always been faithful to His word. Today many are taking Him at his word. *'Jesus Christ is the same yesterday, today and forever'* (Hebrews 13:8). Jesus heals today (See Part Five). His message is working for

believers just as it did 2,000 years ago. As born again believers, we can appropriate God's resurrection life into our mortal bodies and be made whole. Paul said, *'If the spirit of him who raised Jesus from the dead is living in you, he who raised Christ from the dead will also give life to your mortal bodies through his spirit who lives in you'* (Romans 8:11). Believers are finished with Satan's government. They are in a different kingdom. They are under new government living by faith in all that God has said. That includes their health. God may allow them to see a doctor or surgeon for their medical needs but if God was able to care for his people medically in the wilderness under the old covenant, how much more should we be expecting to enjoy this life in God under the new covenant. On that basis there is much less reliance upon the doctor, let alone dangerous wandering in the confusing maze of spiritual alternatives.

2. Satan

The spiritual alternative to Jesus can only be this one source. Satan and his demon spirits pervert the truth of God's word. He invades both medical science and those who think they have found God but have not. Indeed we have reached the point where we do well to check out the spiritual status of those who seek to heal us both in the surgery and indeed in some churches. He takes advantage of those who don't know Jesus in a personal way and who don't have the Holy Spirit living in them.

But beware! There are counterfeit healers about, *'false apostles, deceitful workmen, masquerading as apostles of Christ. And no wonder, for Satan himself masquerades as an angel of light'* (2 Cor. 11:13–14). Satan deceived Adam and Eve. He seeks to deceive us today. He is in opposition to God. He counterfeits the things of God. He seeks to draw people to him and bring them eternal death. Satan's 'healing', including much of 'alternative medicine', is one of his main deceptions in these days.

23

Do these occult healing methods work?

They very often do work. If it suits his purpose Satan will 'heal'.

He is unknowingly invited into lives through these 'healing' methods; his price is a devastating one. Our religion, whether in the churches or outside, is for the most part humanist with little idea of the supernatural, whether it be God or Satan. So the question 'does it work?' has the wrong focus. The enormous dangers are missed.

In this secular society few doctors deny the experience of the occasional miracle! It is easy to put it down to God when no scientific reason can be found! Science, and a vague idea of God, are convenient blinds used by Satan. What is really happening to the rest of him as one part of man is being 'healed' by Satan?

In one case a woman with depression was prayed for in a Spiritualist Church. She received temporary relief, but she began to suffer from arthritis. In my own case I was cured of haemorrhoids by a spiritualist 'healer'. This fired my enthusiasm for spiritual power. I soon believed that after death I would return to earth in another body. Thus like so many spiritualists I was led to believe in reincarnation. Satan's wiles had blinded me to the truth of an eternal life spent in heaven or in hell.

One spiritual method is much the same as another, and a big growth area is acupuncture. This is rooted in Taoism, a Chinese spiritual philosophy for which divination was the basis. Divination is spiritual discovery by forbidden magical methods. Also there are more and more 'healers' who can bring a powerful occult touch to an otherwise acceptable practice. One case involved a dental surgeon who treated what he saw as energy imbalances (like the sort deriving from Taoism and seen in acupressure) whilst the patient sat in the dental chair. When he is invited in, however unknowingly, Satan will leave something that was not bargained for.

'But I'm a Christian, and I'm feeling better for my "healing", so am I OK?'

The seed for physical, mental, emotional and spiritual problems is sown by Satan when given access through occult healing. For a born again believer the walk with God is restricted or blocked as darkness takes over from light. Frequently you hear: 'I don't seem to be able to pray in the way that I used to'.

For someone not born again of the Spirit of God, involvement can mean missing the real blessing that God has. In every case it is only the relationship with Jesus Christ, and the call that can be made on Him, that can undo the damage caused. Satan seeks to deceive us all.

Where do we find Satan's 'healing' taking place?

Don't even go looking! Any involvement is a sin. Occult means 'hidden', and according to God's word it should not be investigated. *My* big mistake was to become a 'searcher' into occult healing methods.

'Healers' are to be found everywhere. Some of the most caring people are wanting desperately to bring something they think is good to the world. They are being led into occult techniques. Many are becoming spiritual (or psychic) 'healers' who consult the dead. The truth is that they are not consulting the dead at all. The dead go to heaven or to hell, and the Bible allows no possibility of communication. Satan impersonates the dead and he is deceiving them.

This 'healing' is increasingly found in thousands of front rooms, in Spiritualist Churches and even in some churches where religion is allowed to take the place of Jesus Christ. It is found too in 'Healing' and 'Help' centres opening up throughout the country.

What else does the Bible say about Satan's 'healing'?

'*For our struggle is not against flesh and blood, but against the rulers, against the authorities, against the powers of this dark world and against the spiritual forces of evil in the heavenly realms*' (Ephesians 6:12) – not against men but against Satan, the person in control of today's sorcerers, spiritists and magicians.

The following are some of the Scriptures relatinq to sorcery, spiritism and witchcraft (and the same things by any other name): Ex. 7:11–12; Ex. 22: 18; Lev. 19:26, 31; Lev. 20:6, 27; Zech. 10:2; Mal. 3:5; Acts 8:9; Acts 16:16; Acts 19:19; 1 Sam. 28; 1 Chron. 10:13–14; Is. 2:6; 8:19; Jer. 27:9–10; Gal. 5:20; 2 Tim. 3:8; Rev. 21:8; Rev. 22:15.

2: The current thinking

'Healing' and 'Help' centres

There is a fast growth of these centres where occult healing methods are included in the range of alternative treatments. These centres may be residential, or not. They can be profit-making or voluntary. They are not of course to be confused with the Medical Centres where the medical profession is to be found, but they are increasingly gaining credibility, support and approval from influential people.

In these stressful times man is full of uncertainty about death; whilst he is alive he is full of uncertainties about his health. Satan knows this. Anxieties remain whether the staff at the Centre are charming and friendly or whether they are not; whether the treatment is free or expensive; and whether patients actually 'feel' better or whether they don't. More important: when the occult is involved, the 'extras' and the 'approval' only serve Satan's purposes. The care, the good diet, and the peace of the place only encourage patients to continue. Whatever the outward appearances, Satan moves into any establishment where an occult technique gives him an opening. Satan is no respecter of persons. Spiritual activity not in line with the revelation of the Bible, and not in Jesus' name, is an open invitation to him.

What do today's leaders have to say?

Slowly a public awareness is dawning even if based mainly upon the horror stories that abound following experiences with the occult. The Bishop of Gloucester wrote in his *Diocesan Gazette* (July, 1983) about false and corrupt perversions:

> 'They are not sanctioned, and in many cases are roundly condemned, by scripture, Christian tradition, and reason alike, and Christians are best advised to steer well clear of them all from horoscopes and ouija boards to seances and so-called healings by means of occult practices or magical devices.'

Then beneath the Bishop's message, and as if to evidence the spiritual warfare being waged in these days, there appeared a private letter lifting up a cancer help centre as a place glorifying to God. At that centre treatments described in Part Two of this book are practised. The *Gazette* reflected both sincerity and confusion. Man's reason and tradition need to be supplanted by God's wisdom if Satan's schemes are to be stopped.

Sincerity in these matters is irrelevant. A sincere person unknowingly on the devil's side, is a dangerous counsellor. Satan is real. He is alive. He is very sincere! He knows God's word inside out. Ignorance of it is no defence. The truth is in God's Word, *not* in man's sincerity, *not* in man's traditions, *not* in man's reasoning and *not* in any of man's ideas about what he thinks is good. Ministers often say 'Focus on God'. That's right as far as it goes, but we can't afford to ignore Satan. Ministers often approve of yoga and of divining (whether for water or for 'healing' purposes). They have been deceived. Yoga and divination are spiritual; indeed yoga is a form of worship. Such things are 'detestable to the Lord'.

Paracelsus was a very famous occultist, animist, alchemist, diviner, astrologer and magician who lived 500 years ago. Like most today he did not look to God. He looked to himself and the natural world for his remedies. He unknowingly joined Satan's side in the spiritual war. He pointed to nature as the source superior to the Bible. The deceptions of Paracelsus gain ground today. The scholarly encyclopaedias enable Christians to identify Paracelsus as a man working with the counterfeits defined in Deuteronomy 18:10–12. However, and in distinction to the message of this book, read what the Prince of Wales, then President of the British Medical Association, told the doctors at their conference in December 1982:

'But what kind of man was Paracelsus? A charlatan or a gifted healer? In my view he was far from being a charlatan. In this, the 150th anniversary of the B.M.A. we could do worse than look again briefly at the principles he so desperately believed in, for they have a message for our time: a time in which science has tended to become estranged from nature – and that is the moment when we should remember Paracelsus. Above all he maintained there were four pillars on which the whole heart of healing rested. The first was philosophy; the second astronomy (or what we might now call psychology); the third alchemy (or biochemistry) and the fourth virtue (in other words the professional skill of the doctor)'. He then went on to outline the basic qualifications for a doctor: 'like each plant and metallic remedy the doctor too must have a specific virtue. He must be intimate with nature. He must have the intuition which is necessary to understand the patient, his body, his disease. He must have the "feel" and the "touch" which make it possible for him to be in sympathetic communication with the patient's spirits. Paracelsus believed that the good doctor's therapeutic success largely depends on his ability to inspire the patient to confidence and to mobilize his will to health. By the way, he also recommended

chastity and fasting to heighten diagnostic
sensitiveness and to intensify one's hypnotic power!'

No Paracelsian philosophy, no royal or clerical approval,
no measure of care or concern can counter the great and
inevitable dangers in store for those who fall for the wiles
of Satan.

The growth of the occult in Britain was helped in 1952
by the repeal of the Witchcraft Act. This made Britain
one of the most liberal countries in the Western world.
More recently the World Federation of Healers was
granted government approval to treat patients in NHS
hospitals. The Federation comprises largely of professed
mediums.

It will remain to be seen whether alternative medicine
is to become a political issue in Britain. The costs are
low compared to what the NHS can offer from medical
science, and many of the unemployed are setting up as
therapists. Michael Meacher, MP, the Labour Party's
shadow spokesman for Health and Social Security,
seemed to put his weight behind the movement when he
opened the Alternative Medicine Exhibition in 1984.

On the international scene, at the United Nations in
1973, the much-respected World Health Organisation
(WHO) recommended that the medical profession accept
the validity of native cures like those used by witchdoctors. The place of the WHO in the end-time scenario is
looked at in Chapter Eighteen.

The truth of what God says borne out by experience

Kurt Koch is a recognised authority on sorcery and
demonology. In *Occult Bondage and Deliverance* he writes
that anyone who enters Satan's territory, however
unknowingly, will immediately be harassed by the
powers of darkness. They will feel the effects in different
areas of life. He described Harry Edwards as one of the

most dangerous healers in the Western world. He writes that he has come across thousands of cases in which contact with the occult was the root cause of the problem. In nine out of ten cases it was clear occult involvement had played some part.

Christian ministers would do well to note the increasing need for deliverance in Jesus' name.

3: Baptism by the Holy Spirit and discernment

Healing power in the name of Jesus

Jesus wants us to repent of our sins and to seek a relationship with Him. He wants us to be born again, to be baptised by the Holy Spirit and to take the power and authority that is available in His name. Until that happens there can be simply warning in this book. However when we turn to God 'like little children', there can be revelation on what is written here and on what is written in Scripture.

> *The man without the Spirit does not accept the things that come from the Spirit of God for they are foolishness to him and he cannot understand them, because they are spiritually discerned.* (1 Corinthians 2:14).
> *. . . after me will come one who is more powerful than I . . . He will baptise you with the Holy Spirit and with fire.* (Matthew 3:11).
> *But the Counsellor, the Holy Spirit, whom the Father will send in my name, will teach you all things and will remind you of everything I have said to you.* (John 14:26).
> *But you will receive power when the Holy Spirit comes upon you; and you will be my witnesses . . . to the ends of the earth.* (Acts 1:8).

The Scriptures are for today. By the power of the Holy Spirit they can speak to us today. (See 'Divine Healing' in Part Five.)

One sister in the Lord whom I knew, was born again

and within four months of receiving Jesus she took the gospel to the 'headhunters' of the Philippines. God equipped her with the scripture in Mark 16: 15–20:

> He said to them, 'Go into all the world and preach the good news to all creation. Whoever believes and is baptised will be saved, but whoever does not believe will be condemned. And these signs will accompany those who believe: In my name they will drive out demons; they will speak in new tongues; they will pick up snakes with their hands; and when they drink deadly poison, it will not hurt them at all; they will place their hands on sick people, and they will get well'. After the Lord Jesus had spoken to them, he was taken up into heaven and he sat at the right hand of God. Then the disciples went out and preached everywhere, and the Lord worked with them and confirmed his word by the signs that accompanied it.

Through this sister hundreds came to know Jesus. They were born again and baptised by the Holy Spirit. They received the Kingdom of God like little children. 'Anyone who will not receive the Kingdom of God like a little child will never enter it' (Mark 10:15). The natives received the message. They turned from their idols and false gods, and hundreds were instantly healed of dreadful diseases. Jesus healed exactly according to his word in Mark 16. The greatest miracle was that they were born again.

The Bible is borne out by what she and many others in these days know by their own experiences. 'Jesus Christ is the same yesterday, today and forever'. (Hebrews 13:8).

The spiritual dimension: the problem of the intellect

There is relatively little written about Satan's involvement with 'healing'. One of the problems is with the intellectual aspects. Also most of those who have looked into Satan's spiritual realm in a deep way are still there in that place. As far as I am aware, all but one of my many friends and acquaintances from the days of 'healing' are still there – in that same spiritual realm. The deceived cannot be witnesses.

When a patient is 'healed' of a complaint and says he is better or that he feels better, even the believer can have difficulty in speaking out against it! That 'Satan himself masquerades as an angel of light' is a truth to which we believers seem easily blinded. On top of that, the intellect has to deal with the mixture of science and nature, of God and Satan, in the proliferation of 'alternative medicines' that are available. How do we explain our lack of joy when Granny or one of our dearest friends tells us of a release from pain, since the acupuncture, since the reflexology or since she went to see 'that nice lady' who laid hands on her? We can only seek God's guidance in each situation.

There is no intellectual explanation in terms that Granny will be likely to understand readily, and there is a danger in explaining what acupuncture needles are supposed to do. They will be deceptive explanations. The intellect will understand the needles, the energy flows and much else from the acupuncturist's explanations. The intellect will often marry them up with some understanding of science. The true intellectual and spiritual explanation will present difficulty to those whom Satan has involved. The idea of an occult root will present a problem to Granny or to our friend, whatever their natural level of grasping problems might be. In the spiritual dimension we are concerned both with the root in the history of a particular discovery and with any occult involvement of the practitioner himself. Any intellectual exercise can be useful only when directed to finding this out.

The surest answer is given to the spirit that is right with God. Seeing that the promoters of alternative health methods are fast gaining recognition by medical science it becomes increasingly necessary to check the spiritual status of those who treat us.

Discernment

Discernment is essential in a Christian fellowship. I believe discernment is given when the need is there, when we are open and seeking to receive. I believe we have to begin! Having taken the first step more will be given when we show we are prepared to trust God and receive. As Christians we often act on this witness of the Holy Spirit in our own lives but we often deny God by passing it off as intuition. Often I hear: 'I would steer clear of acupuncture (or whatever) but I don't know why'. Of course Satan can pervert anything, but most often I believe Christians' intuition is of God! When we acknowledge Him, He will often confirm it; our confidence is built up, and we move on. God gives us more. Confronted by mountains of deceptive information, often we don't dare recognise that it's God's voice (and why shouldn't it be when we are moving in His Spirit?). We stand aside and watch 'alternative medicine' grow.

These are urgent times and it is clear that enormous numbers of people across the world are coming into the spiritual dimension. Many are being baptised by the Holy Spirit; on the other hand there is a rapid acceleration in the growth of the occult – not only 'alternative medicine' but everything occult.

Children are coming into the spiritual dimension before their parents, through drugs and through rock music and discos. However, the Holy Spirit is giving Christians a new awareness. Rock music is an example. It has been at last rumbled by discerning Christians! How could Christians have been blinded for so long? Some of the lyrics actually praise Satan. Many a Christian Mum and Dad has neglected to see what their children are into. We are offended by the noise and the behaviour so we keep away. We don't of course see the drugs our children use. We don't hear the lyrics. We don't understand the spiritual significance of the beat, and we wrongly suppose it isn't significant. We don't understand the effects of the strobe lighting and we have perhaps never endured it long enough ourselves to see its effects. The truth is that the kids receive the beat and the lyrics even if they themselves aren't aware of them. Satan understands! Ask the witchdoctors in Africa who call up spirits with the same beat!

Many hang on to 'Christian' rock but the Holy Spirit is moving through this whole area. This is still a controversial area among Christians. However, consider what is common to *all* rock music. An occult beat and certain strobe lighting effects cannot be neutralised by Christian lyrics whether they are clearly audible or not.

In the world's view, rock and disco are far removed from the quiet of Transcendental Meditation. Taking a spiritual view, they have everything in common! The extremes of noise and peace are hardly the relevant factors. In both we 'switch off.'

Satan is into everything! The Bible says he is the ruler of this world (1 John 5:19). Discernment is essential. Jesus won the victory over Satan and those who know Jesus are in the Kingdom of God. However, Satan still has to be taken very seriously by Christians. Power over him is given to those who will receive it, and in order to know the enemy when we see it, God gives His people discernment.

'Focus on Jesus' doesn't mean 'ignore Satan'!

The battle is against Satan (Eph. 6:12). Therefore we must not ignore him. The discernment we need to identify him is not an intellectual exercise. It is given to the heart or to the spirit, and Satan would cloud it at the first opportunity. Yet he is more than an opportunist; Satan is a planner!

An easy way to play into Satan's hands is to continue to talk his language when we are in the Kingdom of God.

It serves Satan's purposes to speak of 'seeing Granny' when what someone has seen is a ghostly ectoplasmic manifestation of Granny created by demons. It serves his purpose to talk of energy lines when talking about acupuncture. They don't exist. The ghost of Granny wasn't Granny either! Granny is spending her eternity with the Lord if she knew Him. Otherwise she is spending it separated from Him. Either way, Scripture allows no opportunity for her to return. Satan brings about these manifestations according to the access he has gained and the faith in him. How much better to have that faith that comes by hearing, and hearing by the Word of God (Romans 10:17).

It is often heard (and it is said to me): 'you talk too much of Satan'. Often people can't say the word 'Jesus' before they come to know Him. Indeed typically there is surprise at hearing the name of Jesus except when used blasphemously. Satan wants to stop the use of the name because there is power in that name. By the same token, among Christians, Satan doesn't want his own name mentioned. In fact Satan's Secret Service would like the whole spiritual dimension to be unknown. I was forty-four years of age before I knew that dimension existed. I might have talked about it as I had talked about Jesus, but I didn't know that dimension in either realm, and I didn't know Jesus. I was *en route* to hell without even knowing it.

We can speak without fear about Satan; quite apart from binding him in Jesus' name. Satan deceives undiscerning Christians with the suggestion that to speak of him is to glorify him. On the contrary it is glorifying to him when we ignore him, or accept his deceptions. Satan is the father of such lies and manifestations. It is the way of the world ruled by Satan to receive the counterfeit faith and to glorify him by acknowledging his lies. The Bible tells us to put on the armour of God and cast out Satan. It tells us to receive the true faith that comes from hearing the Word of God.

Certainly occult 'alternative medicines' are not for discussion apart from prayer. The narrative for each therapy in Part Two of the book has been kept to a minimum. Not all the therapies are known to me; the Holy Spirit counselled on what was needed for my walk with the Lord. That same Holy Spirit raised Jesus from the dead. He always gives the same answers to those who seek.

May God give his body the much needed discernment. May we receive also from Him the help needed to act on the truth revealed to us, and may the truth be broadcast throughout the church.

Before looking at particular techniques and schemes

Satan's schemes extend to all of us. He tailors them to our lifestyle. The most dangerous techniques among the 'alternative medicines' are as dangerous as the ouija board and tarot reading.

It cannot be over-emphasised that there is nothing that is really special about any particular technique where the occult is involved. They all involve faith in something supernatural, Satan and not God. When someone in every street is into acupuncture, it is easier for the unbeliever to turn to acupuncture! Satan can accommodate us (and get an entrée) with anything we put our faith in that is not of God.

Jesus said '. . . *Know the truth and the truth will set you free*' (John 8:32). The truth is in God's Word and it cannot be arrived at by any sort of academic exercise. Occult alternative medicines are summed up in one word – Satan. Satan knows all about science too; he's in on it! The spiritual warfare is hotting up and the only way to fight the battles is with the weapons and armour that God provides (Ephesians 6:10–18). However, the guide to various therapies that I have included in Part Two should be helpful. This was written after some prayerful consideration to determine how far to relate Satan's deceptions and 'so-called deep secrets' (Revelation 2:24). Romans 16:19 also tells us: *'Everyone has heard about your obedience, so I am full of joy over you; but I want you to be wise about what is good, and innocent about what is evil.'*

Not all 'alternative medicine' is founded in the occult; I believe most of it is. The task of the discerning Christian is to sound the alarm or the 'all clear' as the Lord leads. It may seem unfair to include the medicines and techniques against which there is no evidence. But, for example, who knows which 'herbal concoctions' might be OK? God knows. If we earnestly desire to know, we can listen to Him. We tend to know the answer when we are considering treatment for ourselves or our dear ones!

4: A Searcher's Path

One day I was given a peace I had never known. The next day, against incredible odds and without any human planning, I was reunited with a movement called Moral Rearmament (MRA), exactly at the place I had last met with it some twenty years previously.

I had never forgotten MRA's four absolute moral standards (absolute honesty, absolute purity, absolute unselfishness and absolute love) and I had tried to build my life upon them. I had failed and now I saw the answer in fellowship with MRA people. I didn't know that without Jesus I was bound to fail. However I was fired with the idea of 'doing good'! Next came my introduction to spiritual healing. It was all in Satan's plan.

An MRA conference in Switzerland provided the forum for many religions. MRA accommodated me at a Rosicrucian* hotel. My particular friends there were some distinguished Hindus. Their peace as well as their moral stance greatly attracted me. Unwittingly they had served an extraordinary purpose in my life and I flew on

* The Rosicrucians are a cult and they believe everything occurs by cosmic, natural law. They tell us that the touch of letters and objects can immediately convey impressions of the sender and of past events. They say the human consciousness can be instantaneously extended out of the body to remote places and events, and that mental impressions and sight and sound sensations can be communicated at a distance without physical means. They believe thoughts can be changed into things and that we can mentally create useful realities from our ideas. All this is occult. Paracelsus was a Rosicrucian.

to my next venue in Scotland for five days of training to become a healer with one of today's outstanding spiritual healers.

By this time I had already been instantaneously 'healed' of haemorrhoids after suffering them for twenty-one years. Little did I realise what the spiritual side-effects of that and my other spiritual involvements would be. Every step I took opened me further to the wiles of Satan. I visited mediums and attended healer training sessions, where I first discovered some of the therapies described in this book. I visited the shrine of Sai Baba, an Indian god-man with counterfeit miracle healing powers. Later I believed I was in communication with his spirit when I received a clear manifestation of his presence. Eventually I prayed to him, and I believed that after my death I would be reincarnated in another body.

Without realising it, I had become a full-time 'searcher'. I read 'The Life of Jesus', a rich red leather edition of 1884. Also, still as a searcher, I became a regular church attender once again.

In my search I was close to others who were treading the same path. One of these friends became tormented in a dreadful way. I didn't then know about demons; however, he was seeing them. A week later he was found dead. Immediately I went to a Spiritualist Church. Here the medium perfectly described the red leather book to me. 'I have the previous owner with me,' she said. 'Ask your wife. She will know. It is a very important book.' A clever choice of book for the demons to describe! Satan was masquerading as an angel of light. The medium had also described the extraordinary hands of the original owner. I told my wife and she found a snapshot of this old family friend taken some forty years before. The big hands could be seen just as she remembered them. Previously cool about my search, which was now into its second year, she was at last very interested.

The next day we learned *how* my searcher-friend had died – naked with cuts and bruises. As with the

41

demon-possessed man among the tombs in Mark 5:5, they were self-inflicted. Satan's purpose is to bring death, and this he had done. My wife's interest in searching lasted only twenty-four hours!

After eighteen months of working on MRA's absolute standards in my life, and as a searcher, I hastily began looking into the dangers. God overruled Satan's intention for my life. By a great miracle I was born again, and God showed me that my healing methods were from Satan.

For twenty years the MRA book *Remaking Men* by Paul Campbell and Peter Howard, had been my 'bible.' As a Christian I renounced my healing involvement; but *not* MRA. Then eventually David Watson wrote this in a letter to me: 'I saw red lights when I read *Remaking Men*, because of the absence of any reference to Christ. Any movement that purports to proclaim Christ must be unashamedly Christ-centred in its writings and proclamations. The very desire to open doors to all faiths is also its definite weakness, and I would not be happy if any Christian got involved in MRA.' Long after I received it, the Lord eventually got through to me by means of that letter. I was set free.

Many, including committed Christians, have turned from drugs to spiritual solutions in the belief that they were natural therapies. I pray the Lord will use the words and Scriptures in this book to set more people free.

PART TWO
ALTERNATIVE MEDICINE:
A GUIDE

The witness of the Holy Spirit is vital. Aside from that, any so-called 'intellectual' approach is to be found in either the occult origin (or root) or in the nature of any practitioner's involvement contrary to God's word.

In this guide to more than one hundred therapies, it is hoped that Christian readers will be helped to discern themselves whether a particular treatment is of God or not.

Why have I included therapies that are *not* founded in the occult? The answer is that an increasing number of their practitioners are bringing an occult dimension into the therapy. This is particularly true the further we move away from so-called scientific medicine. Perhaps surprisingly, we find less of an intellectual barrier to the utter illogicality of some treatments that are offered. Satan has made his mark on medical science in many ways, and particularly through drugs, but in these days Satan appears to be focusing on alternative therapies subtly designed for an unsuspecting public.

Why then don't I explain each technique? One answer is that I could not do so, even if I believed it would be right. Perhaps one day there will be huge volumes connecting the foundation of, say, reflexology with the systems we see today. But I doubt it! Attempts will be made, but the philosophies often go back more than 5,000 years, and there are new therapies every year. God gives His people a much simpler way!

What can be understood is that nearly all the therapies are in one way or another based upon subtle spiritual implications. Most are derived from the occult, humanistic or religious world views of their originators. This means they stem from a belief system that is contrary to

God. In the words of Brooks Alexander of the American research organisation, Spiritual Counterfeits Project: '. . . the metaphysical framework from which they (the Eastern or occult healing techniques) emerge, is so pervasive and encompassing that every detail of practice is intricately related to elements of the underlying belief system. As a result the technique taken as a whole will carry overtones and implications of the metaphysical system from which it is derived, even if that system is not explicitly attached.'*

One of the most often reiterated biblical themes is that we should guard ourselves against deception and separate ourselves from counterfeit spirituality; it is not God's will that we should search for truth among the hidden knowledge. God will give discernment to those who earnestly seek it.

There are two errors in dealing with Satan. One is to deny his existence and power. That is the error of the great majority in these days. The other error is one that we must avoid falling into in the area of alternative medicine: the idea that Satan and his demons are active everywhere and in everything. There is a danger that we can be led into fearing a treatment because Satan *might* be in it – in the therapy through the therapist. For example, where herbal remedies are concerned, there can be the error of ascribing to Satan something that is from the Lord.

Jesus calls Satan 'the prince (or ruler) of this world' (John 14:30). Satan is the ruler over the affairs of the world and in opposition to God. However the earth is the Lord's and we can confidently use the things that He provides in His creation, giving thanks to Him for them. *'For everything God created is good, and nothing is*

---

* Reprinted by permission of Spiritual Counterfeits Project, Inc. © 1978. P.O. Box 4308, Berkeley, California 94704, U.S.A. 'Holistic Health from the Inside' (*Spiritual Counterfeits Project Journal* – August 1978).

to be rejected if it is to be received with thanksgiving, because it is consecrated by the word of God and prayer.' (1 Timothy 4:4–5). Whilst we should not use any herb or treatment because it has been 'improved' by magic, and whilst we would not allow treatment by a therapist who, however innocently, was seen to resort to occult power, we are free to use the goodness of the Lord's creation – the plants, the minerals, the animals and all that is in it.

'God did not give us a spirit of timidity, but a spirit of power, of love and of self-discipline' (2 Timothy 1:7). Fear is from Satan, and being alert to the wiles of Satan doesn't mean we have to fear him or even pay undue attention to him. Once again, we know that herbal remedies are good and we have the authority of Scripture; therefore unless we get a check in our spirit, or *know* of an occult addition to what God has provided, we are only glorifying Satan when we start to worry or fear.

For therapies where there is some clear occult connection, whether from what is written or from a practitioner's own literature, it will be up to individual Christians to make their decisions. For other therapies, where there is an openness to occult adaptation by the practitioner, Christians can know in their spirits if something is not right; once again the Christian will be free to make a decision. When the Holy Spirit convicts us, we are free to do something about it. Fear however can only be from Satan; our response is to praise the Lord, and, if necessary, bind Satan in the name of Jesus (Matthew 12:29).

It is true that the mere sight of some therapies (usually the complex or little known ones) mentioned in print in a book like this can lead some to deliverance. In my personal testimony on homoeopathy in Chapter Nine it will be seen that the Lord used a Christian book to start off a long chain of confirmations of the occult basis of homoeopathy. The book hadn't said homoeopathy was occult, but the Holy Spirit did! Taking an example from the First Edition of my own book, one reader, encouraged to scan through the book in the course of deliverance ministry spotted 'chiropractic'. Now I don't write that chiropractic is occult; however, the fact is that *some* chiropractic treatments are. Practitioners can add something more! As she describes in her testimony in Chapter Five, this person received deliverance and healing. Jesus calls driving out demons, 'a miracle' (Mark 9:38–39) and we are seeing more miracles in these days. Praise His wonderful name!

Seeing the names of therapies in this book may prompt responses such as the above. Yet in other cases therapies like chiropractic may well quite rightly produce no response at all from those, like myself, who have been treated by a chiropractor. Alas, seeing a name might even promote fear! It is no part of my purpose to encourage Satan by referring to therapies in which he is not making any impression! However, it is right, I believe, to include a range of *all* therapies (good and bad) in order to warn that even the best, like physiotherapy, are in these days open to abuse by therapists who, choosing to use occult power, combine other techniques.

The Holy Spirit is the teacher (Luke 12:12). New therapies are showing themselves all the time. Some are so new that nothing is written about them. Some therapies are backed by doubtful philosophy that the practitioner himself may never have resorted to. It is neither easy nor useful to give more information for all the therapies. However I believe it is clear which therapies are so clearly occult that discerning Christians will unreservedly reject them. Furthermore in their own situations, where there is a need to know, Christians can hear the answer when they earnestly seek it.

5: So-called physical therapies

The area of so-called 'new' therapies includes *acupuncture*. The present basis for it was provided by the philosophical school of Taoism founded in the third and fourth centuries B.C. It even dates back 2,000 years before that in ancient China.

Ancestor worship, common in China, has led to sorcery. Their concept of a unity between the universe and man, is common ground with the Hindu and other eastern religions. Thanks in large part to missionary zeal, China now has many Bible-believing Christians. However, undiscerning Christians have brought back much of the demonic that still has not been identified and cast out in the name of Jesus! At one time, acupuncture, used for anaesthesia in China, was refused for the westerners that lived there. It didn't work as well with them! Self-hypnosis and suggestion probably plays an important part, and with the faith in acupuncture in the west in these days, anaesthetic by acupuncture on westerners is now said to be working much better.

There are two basic deceptive beliefs: the existence of energy *ch'i* and the presence of invisible energy lines (meridians) that are supposed to direct the energy to all organs of the body. Drawings of different so-called energy lines are to be found in many occult 'healing' techniques. The energy is said to be controlled by the *yin* and the *yang*, two universal opposing yet harmonising forces, which like negative and positive, and male and female permeate all nature. The imbalance of the *yin* and the *yang* is said to hinder the energy flow and cause illness. Practitioners identify some hundreds of acupuncture

47

'points' along the 'meridian', and they believe that puncture by the needles rebalances the energy and restores health. Although never to be understood, acupuncture is well known today and has been pretty well exposed by Christian writers. Christians have to steer well clear of its occult influence.

Auriculotherapy is a variation of acupuncture, and *acupressure* is rooted in the same philosophy. It involves pressure rather than needles, and so finds favour among the squeamish! Thus it is more acceptable, but equally devastating in its spiritual side-effects. Another energy-balancing therapy, is *moxibustion*. A smouldering fragment of a plant is put on the acupuncture point. The variations can be endless. More creative therapists are into hitting the acupuncture points with laser beams and ultra-sound! A world that has quickly come to accept ideas of meridians and ch'i, readily moves on to more obvious magical practices using the same language. An example is *jin shin do*.

Emile Kremer* summarises the position the Christian has to take in the following way: 'The origin, nature and development of acupuncture . . . show clearly that believers dare not expose themselves to the influence of the spirits that have inspired this ancient healing method which is now sweeping through western countries. . . . They are finding the western nations well prepared through all the forms of occultism (superstitions, astrology, witchcraft, etc) which are spreading very rapidly in so-called Christian countries.'

Christians need to be aware of the activities of cults and of occult practices apart from occult healing therapies, in order to counsel others and take a clear stand as witnesses to the truth found in God's word. The Bible tells us, *'the coming of the lawless one will be in accordance with the work of Satan displayed in all kinds of counterfeit*

* 'Eyes Opened to Satan's Subtlety' by Emile Krémer (M.O.V.E. Press – 1969).

miracles, signs and wonders, and in every sort of evil that deceives those who are perishing.' (2 Thess. 2:9–10).

The whole range of occult therapies includes many that overlap one with another. There are obvious overlaps, too, with the cults and other occult practices. Satan doesn't arrange his wiles in tidy compartments and there is no way that language can adequately describe this spiritual realm. Chapter Ten contains a list of areas that may be helpful in Christian counselling, in order to identify occult involvement. Some understanding of a therapy or occult involvement will often be desirable and I have, I believe, written more than enough about acupuncture in this and previous pages, to establish the status it must have with Christians. An undue interest in the detail is often far from desirable. It is the 'Way Out' that is most important! This is through *renunciation* of the therapy, *repentance* of involvement with it, and *faith in Jesus Christ and His atoning blood*. The help of other Christians filled with the Holy Spirit may also be needed by those who are deeply affected, in order that the powers of Satan can be rebuked, and healing and deliverance brought to them in the name of Jesus.

Once again, *reflexology* is traceable back to China 5,000 years ago. It was also known in ancient Egypt. Practitioners believe there are ten energy channels, each covering all the organs in a zone of the body. By feeling the feet they believe they can find which channel is blocked; then they massage the feet seeking to restore the energy flow. I have studied and done this myself. There has perhaps been little detailed research into the origins, beyond what millions are reading in modern-day 'alternative health' guides. There is enough for the discerning Christian!

Again along similar lines, and perhaps originating in Europe, there is *polarity therapy*. Away from Taoism and China now, it is necessary to look for other clues to the occult root. Its founder made an extensive study of eastern medicine and his spiritual inspiration came from

India. Polarity therapists believe there are five centres in the body (the etheric, the air, the fire, the water and the earth) and that they need to be balanced in order for the energy to flow. The energy charts are once again different. Is it not pure deception?

The question for the intellect is: What, if any, is the scientific basis for these ideas? And, if there is none, from what spiritual kingdom do they come? They are not like electric current – unseen, difficult to understand, but understood by the scientist. They belong to the spiritual dimension.

Yoga is not merely a physical therapy. All those who practise it come under the influence of its occult powers. This is so whether or not there is any awareness of its Hindu origin and whether or not it is the intention not 'to go too far!' It is very dangerous.

I practised yoga myself. However it wasn't until researching more detail for this book that I discovered the true extent of yoga's influence in Britain. I was put in touch with an organisation called 'Friends of Yoga', a branch of an Indian registered trust.

The Vice-President of Friends of Yoga wrote to me: 'Yoga is *not* a religion, but all religions have their roots in yoga philosophy, including Christianity.' She wrote, 'Christ himself was one of the greatest Bhakti/Karma yogis that ever lived. The Surya Namaskar (Salute to the Sun) can be done to the Lord's Prayer, and I learned it this way from a Catholic missionary, who is himself a devoted Christian and a practising yogi.'

The truth is that yoga aims to liberate us from the normal human condition and to replace this with a 'higher state of consciousness' in which man can see himself as divine. There is nothing Christian about it. Yoga can never be safe. It can affect body and soul, as well as bringing eternal danger to the spirit. It aims to let the supposed 'latent element' or 'true self' within man shine out as god. It is a counterfeit.

We don't easily learn the lessons of Adam and Eve

50

and the fall of man. *'The serpent said to the woman "You will surely not die. For God knows that when you eat of it your eyes will be opened, and you will be like God, knowing good and evil." '* It was Satan's lie. The truth is in God's word. The Holy Spirit living in those who know Jesus as Saviour and Lord is quite different from the yoga idea of man being divine. There is no latent element in man; we are nothing until we receive Jesus. *'. . . to all who received him, to those who believed in his name, he gave the right to become children of God.'* (John 1:12).

Hinduism is the prevailing world view in the west today and every yoga teacher can be seen as a Hindu or Buddhist missionary. Christianity is quickly and progressively being eliminated from western schools, and the emphasis is shifting to teaching about other people's religions. This is overtly done and it supports the Hindu and eastern deceptions that prevail in alternative medicine, the cults and all of the occult.

Those practising yoga don't discover their 'true self'. Rather they progressively open themselves up, through their passivity, to invasion by demons. Sometimes they use a mantra, a name of a Hindu god given to enable contact with him by calling his name or mantra. Of course contact is with the Satanic realm, and I used the mantra *om*. Once the demons take over, they are viewed as the 'god within'.

If those who practise yoga and don't know Jesus, will take the step of faith and ask Jesus to come into their lives, they will be born again and they will become new creations. They will have the Holy Spirit dwelling within them. Only then will yoga practitioners know that what they had before was a counterfeit peace, and that the thief had come only to kill and steal and destroy. Jesus is the one that brings life, and with Him they can have it to the full. (John 10:10).

Again from China, there is *t'ai chi*. As the name suggests, the aim is to tune into the 'ch'i' energy. It seems to be a sort of civilian martial art. Martial arts are

51

an expression of eastern spiritual philosophy. The body is said to have an intrinsic energy, ch'i, which can be developed by special techniques. Faith in this ch'i soon comes to those that participate. Satan is the author of the supernatural powers seen in martial arts; they are *not* energies dormant within us. From India there is Indian Boxing (not very common). From China; Ch'uan-fa or Kung-Fu. From Korea there is Taekwondo. The best known are Judo and Karate; along with many others, they come from Japan.

To the onlooker T'ai Chi looks like a spiritual dance. One practitioner saw it, not only as a means to combat the illnesses of mind and body but as a way of understanding the 'inner nature'. However the understanding that results is that of Tao philosophy. Although T'ai Chi is much older in concept, it is said that the philosophy of T'ai Chi developed from the more elementary idea of defence around the twelfth century.

T'ai Chi means the underlying unity of all manifestation and it is designed to integrate the personality with the spirit by alignment of energies and the opening up of what are seen as higher faculties. In other words practitioners are coming deeper into the Satanic realm, the counterfeit of Christians who receive more light as they walk with Jesus.

It is once again emphasised that the explanation of t'ai chi, yoga, acupuncture, or any of these deceptions, is nothing more than an attempt at some description of the process to the so-called peace, healing and eventual enlightenment that these philosophies promise. The description is as the deceived will see it. The explanations of ch'i, yin, yang, and the endless diagrams that appear in the catalogues and prospectuses of the promoters, are nothing but deception. On first view of such literature Christians may conclude that people must be crazy to fall for it! However Satan has a powerful foothold with many in these days.

From Japan, there is *aikido*, a so-called exercise or movement therapy along the lines of T'ai Chi. These so-called 'soft' or 'internal' martial arts include also a form of karate known as *mushindo karate*. Compared to the 'hard' martial arts described previously, they are much more concerned with mental discipline, meditation and submission to occult power. Thus, and not surprisingly to those who have some awareness of Satan's schemes, it is these gentle drawing room martial arts that are the really powerful ones. These 'soft' varieties are especially dangerous and subtle, but this should not in any way minimise the occult dangers in those more familiar ones that have a spectacular and vigorous element.

Again from Japan, there is *shiatsu* which seems to be akin to acupressure. Shiatsu has been a traditional occupation for the blind in Japan, and now we have seen a course introducing Shiatsu to the blind in Britain at a Tibetan Buddhist Retreat in Cumbria. The Royal National Institute for the Blind (RNIB) inform me: 'With the present general interest in alternative medicine it is natural that several enquiries have been made by visually handicapped persons interested in Shiatsu as a possible career.' The RNIB runs the North London School of Physiotherapy where visually handicapped students are prepared for the examinations of the Chartered Society of Physiotherapy, and the unsighted are in many ways especially suited to this sort of work. It is a tragedy to find the inroads shiatsu is making into this much respected body of unsighted people.

I identify all of the foregoing therapies as ones that Christians will want to avoid. And there are dozens more. What about Rudolf Steiner's *anthroposophical medicine*? Like homoeopathy this is accommodated by the medical profession in Britain. It seems to be a mixture of occult concepts and it is allied to homoeopathy. The first therapeutic centre of its kind in the English-speaking world, offering residential anthroposophical treatment, was opened recently close to my own home.

The origins of *Bach flower remedies* seem also to present a clear case. They consist of 38 remedies prepared from flowers on a formula devised by Dr Edward Bach. They treat negative states of mind which he believed were the causes of any disorder. So far so good! But further enquiry shows that Bach was a diviner. He found that by holding his hand over a flowering plant, if for example he was despondent, it enabled him to find the plant to cure his despondency. The distance Christians put between themselves and Bach remedies (and indeed all of these methods) will be something they have to decide, for themselves.

It is true that much of today's orthodox medicine may be rooted in the occult. Where do you draw the line? Only God can answer individuals on that. Orthodox medicine, with modern drugs, has advanced to the stage where investigation of all its occult roots would be very difficult. The symbol of the British Medical Association includes the serpent!

It may be that some *herbal concoctions* would be appropriate subjects for research. Of course the simple herbs, used in their own right since Bible times, have a God-given healing quality. '*Their fruit will serve for food and their leaves for healing*' (Ezekiel 47:12). However further enquiry is worthwhile where herbal mixtures are founded in magic, where formulae are given by divination, or where herbs are collected as charms are recited. As with orthodox medicine, no sweeping generalisations can be made.

Nicholas Culpepper (1616–1654) was perhaps the most famous of the traditional herbalists. He trained as an apothecary (the forerunner of the GP today). Then he went on in what he believed to be science, combining herbalism with astrology. Astrology is the occult art of deriving knowledge from the stars and their influence on, in Culpepper's case, plant life. In its origin and nature, astrology is idolatrous and Satanic; and so what of the origins of some of the concoctions that Culpepper formulated?

More herbal remedies are today becoming available from the east. *Ginseng*, regarded by the Chinese as a cure-all and a 'gift from the gods' is being heavily promoted at this time. The Chinese and Koreans have used ginseng for over 5,000 years. I mention this herb specifically because it is so highly regarded in the east. What can be said about it? One booklet used for sales promotion tells us the orientals regarded the shape of the root (it closely resembles a human body) as a sign from the powers that be that this was the herb for man. I read that it took six years for it to grow and that a great deal of ceremony surrounds both the planting and the harvesting. It seems there are quality grades. The first is 'Heaven' or 'King', the second grade is 'Earth' and the third is 'Good' or 'Man'. I read that 'vast' research has gone into ginseng since 1854! In conclusion, somewhat surprisingly, I read, '. . . neither is there any evidence that ginseng is able to cure any specific ailment.' Whatever the strange conclusion of this particular sales promotion pamphlet, I don't doubt that hundreds have put their faith in ginseng and seen their symptoms disappear. Needless to say, that is not the point. What of the *hakims* (or 'Wise Men'), the relatively new arrivals from the Indian sub-continent dispensing native herbalism?

The manipulation that is the essential feature of *osteopathy* and *chiropractic* appears to be well founded. However since osteopathy is illegal in countries like Belgium, closer enquiry into these major therapies may well be timely. No condemnation is intended here, but these are days of variety with alternative medicine practitioners, ignorant of the spiritual aspects, looking in on one another's methods. The nature of the treatments given by the osteopath and chiropractor, using the hands almost throughout, leaves any misguided practitioner well open to what Satan is up to in these days. Whilst a 'searcher' in the occult realm of medicine I received training from such a practitioner.

Chiropractic may well be sound as a therapy for spine adjustment, but its practitioners move to dangerous ground when they swallow the energy ideas. Palmer, the founder, identified an energy which he called the 'innate' and he believed its flow through the nervous system could be blocked by spinal misalignments. Osteopathy works on various levels, according to one health guide, and Still, its founder, was, like the acupuncturists, thinking of other body healing forces.

Naturopathy, involving diet, fasting and exercise, can once again be helpful to good health. However this innocent-sounding therapy has come to mean something more than a package of natural treatments. One natural health clinic describes naturopathy very fairly as a holistic approach combining multiple methods best suited to the individual and including the use of diet, fasting, exercises and structural adjustments. However the reality in the centres that are proliferating in these days is that the 'multiple methods' will usually include at least one occult treatment method. Few are alert to the dangers.

Christians are more and more open to the accusation: '. . . but you are condemning nearly everything.' That reality only reflects the depths to which health care has so very recently, and so very quickly, fallen.

Touch for health is born out of chiropractic and ancient eastern knowledge, and is another approach that combines a number of methods. Many of these therapies will understandably involve the counterfeit of the laying-on-of-hands in the name of Jesus, and another is the *Reiki programme*. The idea is that we lay hands and tap a higher frequency of powerful cosmic healing energy. *Biopathy* is yet another synthesis of ancient and modern wisdom, and anyone joining the programme could well meet reflexology, Bach flower remedies, acupuncture, and much else besides.

In these days we can no longer ignore the spiritual status of those who treat us; nevertheless it is emphasised again and again in this book that the mere mention of an alternative treatment is not to be taken as any suggestion that it should necessarily be avoided. However, Christians will want to approach all with caution. Among the best established and admirable of the therapies is *physiotherapy*. The Chartered Society of Phsyiotherapy, in a position paper submitted to the BMA in December 1983, considered many so-called 'alternative' techniques were already available from the physiotherapist within orthodox medical care. The paper acknowledged its interest in recognisable alternatives. I believe the floodgates are open, and the Society should note that many of these alternatives are not what they seem.

The paper makes it clear that the Society has no definition of physiotherapy, 'preferring the term to remain flexible because too rigid a definition would have the effect of imposing potentially restrictive boundaries on the further development of a still growing profession.' The following assessment of the profession by the Chartered Society provides a realistic view of the way it is set to make its contribution to the quiet revolution that is taking place in health care: 'There is now a greater understanding of the significance of the deliberate professional use of touch by chartered physiotherapists and their use of highly skilled manipulative techniques, and of the effectiveness of touch as a means of healing.' There is now a greater understanding of the effectiveness of touch as a means of sensory input and emotional contact and its implications for 'healing'! Physiotherapists must not go too far. The Society has a strong commitment to research in physiotherapy and to developing further the research base, but it needs to know that a loving touch is one thing, and the 'deliberate professional use of touch' for 'healing' can be quite another. It leads to therapy along the lines of therapeutic touch and the paranormal spiritual therapies, which are not from God, and which are looked at in Chapter Seven.

The following is the testimony of Janice, a young Christian woman who, in pain and desperation, went to a physiotherapist who was 'highly recommended' by her friends:

'I was born with legs of slightly uneven length. When I was at university, and in desperation to get back on my feet after a "slipped disc", I visited a physiotherapist. He said he had improved on his physiotherapy treatments through a study of Chinese medicine. He told me how he had overcome paralysis as a boy by sheer will power. I had not then come into the revelation of Jesus' power to heal today, but as I was told more and more of his medical beliefs, I became increasingly worried. On my final visit he held my feet and told me he could learn about the health of the body through doing this. He told me I had had kidney trouble in the past. He was right, for I had kidney stones when I was sixteen. Then he said that when he was massaging a back he could always tell if a person had cancer because he felt something like thick green sludge, and "they" would tell him he could no longer treat the person. Who "they" were, I dreaded to ask! He said he could tell where the pain centres were as he only had to run his hand over my back, two or three inches over my skin, and electric shock went from his hand to the spot. Again he was quite right, and I used to feel it. Finally he told me he practised "astral projection"* and that he could stop and restart his heart at will. I had been baptised by the Holy Spirit before receiving this treatment but as I had not come into correct teaching I didn't listen to the promptings of the Spirit early enough.

'I repented of my involvement with this physiotherapist after reading *The Holy Spirit and You* by Dennis

* Astral projection is an occult experience which involves leaving the body.

58

Bennett. Interestingly, he could never get my back right although I know he never had any problems with a lot of other peoples'! Now I knew he was not only a physiotherapist, but also a spiritualist, a healer and a reflexologist.

'About two years ago my back was badly injured when I lifted some very heavy files at work. My doctor, and a surgeon, said this time the injury was so bad the only thing that could help was surgery, but the chances of success were only fifty-fifty. I was bedridden and in agony, but I was not prepared to take those odds. Recently I had read books on divine healing and was now sure, both in my mind and in my spirit, that it was God's perfect will to heal His children. However, John, my husband, and I were not quite sure how to pray and so to 'buy time' and to get the surgeon 'off my back' while I studied the Scriptures and found someone who believed in divine healing and who would pray in faith, we decided I should undergo some manipulative treatment. I was careful to avoid obvious satanic workers in alternative medicine in choosing someone to provide treatment, but I did not yet realise there were dangers in 'respectable' alternative medicine too.

'One of the elders in our church was visiting a chiropractor and another friend had recently had her back put right by a chiropractor. After four months totally bedridden I began to receive chiropractic treatment. After an initial visit for diagnosis, the chiropractor explained the damage. This is where I think practitioners in alternative medicine especially succeed. They are kind and show understanding to the patient. They explain everything and unlike so many NHS situations they have time to make you feel you matter, which is so very important. The chiropractor explained that I had a cracked vertebra, advanced spondulitis, a twisted pelvis and sacrum, and uneven leg lengths. Six weeks after the treatment began, my pelvis was eventually straightened, but soon it twisted again. John and I were trusting more and more in the Lord for healing and we had twice received instantaneous improvement after praying in faith. However we were still relying on the chiropractor too. Alternative medicine has an insidious draw.

'After six months we took a slow and painful trip to spend a week away. We made the journey equipped with x-rays and the name of a local chiropractor. I needed his "patch up" treatment for the return journey. He told me it was likely I would be crippled by the age of thirty-five. I was then twenty-four. John and I were very depressed. On the journey home the Lord challenged us: "Will you believe this chiropractor's prognosis or will you believe my promise to heal?" It was hard but we knew the Lord was right and we decided to believe Him and not the chiropractor's prognosis. My condition then deteriorated for three weeks! However we pressed into our faith and proclaimed our trust in the Lord.

'At the end of the three weeks we heard of a healing meeting at a local renewal gathering and we asked the Lord if I should go. He marvellously confirmed that I should go and that He would heal me. At the end of the meeting an evangelist prayed with me in Jesus' name. The power of God so flooded through me that it set all my bones into place. It shortened my longer leg as well. I had received my healing.

'Three days later I was due to visit the chiropractor. I had no need of more treatment but wished to show him just what had happened. He was utterly astounded. He was edgy and nervous but had to accept the evidence before him. He confirmed that everything was in place. My doctor too, confirmed that I was healed.

'Although I had finished with the chiropractor, the effects of the treatment with both him and the physio-therapist had not ended in the spiritual realm. Many weeks after I was healed, I suddenly started getting severe sciatica. I realised this was a satanic attack but was not aware of the reason. I contacted two Spirit-filled Christians whom the evangelist recommended, and their discernment was that I needed to be cut off from the effects of the physiotherapist and to receive deliverance. The sciatica left. However I was now receiving a pain in my hip. This seemed like a mirror of what I had once felt there, but not quite like the real thing. They gave me *Beware Alternative Medicine* to read to see if it might jog my memory of any other thing in my past. They knew about the chiropractor but were unsure if that was the cause.

'I began reading Roy Livesey's exposé following the directions for protection by the blood of Jesus. When I got to the section which mentioned chiropractic, I felt something in me leap into my throat and almost a shriek or most urgent whisper in my ear, "No, not that!" I then realised that the suspicions expressed in the book were correct, and that I needed further prayer for deliverance. We called it a "Spirit of Chiropractice" and my friends commanded it to leave in the name of Jesus. The spirit went, and the pain in my hip left with it.

'That was a year ago. I am fit and active, horse riding again and lifting heavy toddlers and babies without trouble and with great joy and praise to His wonderful name.'

Much illness is certainly caused by the way man uses his body and the *Alexander method* aims at personal freedom and health through a voluntarily applied discipline. Then there is *breathing therapy*, *air therapy* and *earth therapy*. Therapies are not necessarily as innocuous as they sound, and these have their place with others in the typical alternative health guide helping to blur the identity of other innocuous-sounding therapies which are either rooted in the occult or from a false religious basis. Breathing! We can usually do that safely enough, but not always. There is a therapy called *holonomic integration breathing* where various techniques from eastern and western psychotherapies, bodywork, cultural and spiritual traditions, can be used. Alternatively there is a healing technique mysteriously described as *rebirthing*.

61

One leaflet describes this as a powerful yet gentle healing method which gives you 'an experience of mastery' in your life. The deep breathing is to enable you to take on board new thoughts that empower you while at the same time letting go of the old thoughts.

Schussler's *tissue salts therapy* reckons body cells can absorb essential salts in small (homoeopathic) doses. As a follower of Hahnemann's homoeopathic methods, his biochemistry involves an occult element. One therapy that appears to be free of the occult is *ionisation therapy*. We are told a concentration of positive ionis in the atmosphere is bad for health. Where the therapist sees the need, there is equipment to produce negative ions.

A good rule is to know the spiritual status of the therapist. By listing *dance therapy*, *art therapy* and *music therapy*, it is easy to appear extreme. The difficulty is with words. No-one will deny that dancing, art and music can be properly therapeutic. There can be sound common sense, but beware psychological excursions linked to these organised therapies. An example is the 'guided imagery', aided by music, that is looked at in Chapter Six. One therapist tells us that cosmic man is like a butterfly emerging from its chrysalis and that his sensitivity has 'not just to be experienced but also to be understood'. We are invited to let ourselves be opened up to the 'subtle worlds of colour and sound.' Indeed we do agree, things are not always what they seem. More and more common are subliminal cassette tapes. One catalogue of 'Peaceful New Age Music' tells us, 'You hear only the music, while absorbing and acting upon the subliminal messages.' What of other relaxing music that the promoters describe as New Age, and induce states of 'inner attunement' and 'healing'? The spiritually blind are coming into the spiritual counterfeits that abound in these days. What is offered *is* attractive. We are in a stressed society and we *do* need to relax. Satan is only too willing to help in this; then he will lead the unwary beyond their expectations. There is no other way but to seek the discernment that is available to those who know Jesus.

Satan knows no boundaries, no neat divisions between one alternative therapy and another, and no careful distinction between a cure and a cosmetic. His purpose is to bring spiritual death. One merchant of so-called *holistic cosmetics* tells us that the human aura seen by clairvoyants and healers as coloured rays comes from the 'vital force' stored in our bodies. The moisturising body oil that is used is said to help restore the balance of body energies.

What about *Bates eyesight training*? Here there is emphasis on the importance of the imagination as an aid to better vision. Faced with a bewildering expansion of alternative treatments Christians will need to take their own view. *Sound therapists* have the idea that every organ has its own frequency of vibration which can be altered by sound waves to produce healing. Are they not blinded by science? *'Although they claimed to be wise, they became fools.'* (Romans 1:22).

Hydrotherapy, the taking of pure spa water, is no doubt harmless to some and valuable to many. The Lord provides this spa water and it is 'good'. What of *aromatherapy*, whether involving herbal medicine at one level or as a relaxing beauty therapy at another? *Macrobiotics* is, on the face of it, selection of diet, but in truth it is a system of choosing food, from Japan, and governed by the principles of yin and yang. A Christian doctor writes 'medically it can be very dangerous, especially for children.' It is an intuitive way of living to remain healthy; it is not the Christian way.

Massage and bodywork therapies often have a religious base and claim to correct energy imbalances. In *zone therapy*, and as we have seen in acupuncture and reflexology, manipulation in certain zones of surface anatomy is said to have a creative effect on some distant organ. However, once again there is no known neurological pathway. In *orgonomy (Reichian therapy)*, the energy is called 'orgone energy', derived from 'orgasm'. Reich believed this energy could be released by uninhibited sexual activity. *Bio-energetics* is a method that involves active and passive exercises. It stresses the body in unfamiliar ways and is a sort of psychotherapy to deal with stress. In *do-in*, the practitioner calls the energy 'universal energy' and he uses massage techniques, rather than needles or anything else, to get a good energy flow. The *Feldenkrais technique* involves 'functional integration'! It uses physical and meditative exercises derived from yoga. *Rolfing* (or 'structural integration') is a method to get correct posture and relieve energy blockages. The patient is subjected to physical pressure, and emotional release is said to occur.

In Britain, therapists enjoy a freedom. New therapists, often with variations on the old therapies, are appearing all the time. There is a greater involvement in all kinds of cult and occult activity, and a selection is listed in Chapter Ten. As a result of this activity the world is made more open to deception by these therapies. Christians should understand that most of these therapists are well meaning and sincere. ' . . . *Our struggle is not against flesh and blood*'; but against the powers of darkness. (Ephesians 6:12). The therapists are deceived by the powers of darkness but they are clear and positive in their objective to bring physical healing. It is no part of their purpose deliberately to deceive Christians. Their literature can be freely read, and they are invariably generous in their explanations of what they seek to do.

The therapies are the spiritual counterfeits to divine healing and as such it is not surprising that most of the therapies are very simple. It is said of the great yogis that when they achieved what they saw as godhood, still they were not satisfied and had to build philosophies around themselves. It is the same with new therapists today. Their philosophies and explanations are not new, and neither were those of the yogis before them. Christians will often find it easy to assess a therapy or therapist on the basis either of what is said or of what is committed to print in leaflets, catalogues, etc. We can look at a therapy as far as we can for ourselves, then when we need to, we can trust God to speak into the situation where we are uncertain.

God made us in such a way that very often healing will naturally take place without any human effort. That, I suggest, is not the 'natural' healing that many ascribe to the therapies I am describing. These therapies usually involve faith, and faith involves a choice between the truth and a lie.

Christians know that the ultimate truth behind all creation is God himself. We put our faith in Him, and that faith 'comes from hearing the message and the message is heard through the word of Christ.' (Romans 10:17). Every area of knowledge that man explores apart from God ends up as a faith system, and in any case man is a reasoning creature who will inevitably put his faith in something.

The faith that is purely in the mind, as distinct from the God-kind of faith which is in the spirit and based upon a sound relationship with Him, is an unsound faith. Many therapies draw upon this sort of faith whatever other occult character they may have.

Even Christian faith teaching can be a road to error; leading Christian teachers have cautioned against misunderstanding it. They have described some faith teaching as a new gnosticism because of its emphasis on knowledge of what we can 'claim' from Scripture, what can be achieved by 'positive confession', and similar techniques. Very often of course there is no fault with the faith teacher; when I was believing for a hundredfold return for a large donation given to one faith teacher early in my Christian life, I didn't get it! Happily Satan isn't always allowed to deliver when Christians start to believe his lies! I had grabbed at Mark 4:20 and claimed the hundredfold return; my belief was in the Scripture. The Scripture would have been the *source* of my faith, but I needed to believe *God*. Many are believing for their healings in the same way, and they remain without their health. Before I really understood the meaning of gnosticism (it means 'knowledge'), the spirit of it was discerned in me, and it was cast out in the name of Jesus. People do perish for lack of knowledge (Hosea 4: 6). I was out of balance and my faith needed to be in Jesus rather than in the good things promised in the Bible; I shall receive these according to the measure of my faith in God to provide them. Jesus said, '*Have faith in God . . . whatever you ask for in prayer, believe that you have received it, and it will be yours.*' (Mark 11:22-24).

The idea of energy is at the root of much of alternative medicine. But what of demons? This so-called energy is what some religions have called God or the 'force'. We are told we are entering a New Age and it is assumed that the increasing scientific research into the paranormal will validate the ideas of this energy and bring a marriage of science and what is being called the New Age movement (the new religion).

While British universities begin to follow the patterns seen in America with research into parapsychology, believing it can be a scientific study, centres are opening up at grass roots level to harness the energy that some academics are only now starting to look at. In one such British New Age Centre, the aim is to bring people together in an atmosphere of harmony and caring, 'to help find a balance within and thus create a greater quality of life for themselves.' They run different workshops. For example in the Crystal Workshop New Agers can experience 'different crystals, flows and energies.' They can learn 'about crystals past and present' and they can 'transform' through crystal meditation and healing! For the more technically minded there are classes and clinics on *mora therapy*. Its proponents expect it to become the medicine of the twenty-first century.

Away from the practitioners themselves and the understanding of energy they are receiving, whether from crystals or from electromagnetic medicine, universities are for the first time taking a real interest. In December 1984 Edinburgh University invited applications for its first Professor of Parapsychology. The press release from the university tells us that the Koestler Chair of Parapsychology will be the first such established professorial post in Britain. It will be part of the Faculty of Social Sciences, and the staff of the internationally-known Department of Psychology, in which the new professor will be located, were said to have unanimously expressed the wish to have the new chair in their department.

The terms of the £500,000 endowment bequest stipulate that the word 'parapsychology' is to be understood to mean the scientific study of 'paranormal phenomena', in particular the capacity attributed to some individuals 'to interact with their environment by means other than the recognised sensory and motor channels.'

Perhaps the new research at Edinburgh will include a study of ley-lines. Occultists believe that ley-lines carry energy in the earth and give it out to people and other life on the planet. I have myself spent time on the Scottish hillsides with my pendulum looking for these ley-lines! Then there is the energy that some believe influences the water diviner's rod; many a churchgoer is blind to the evil of water divining, and of course these things *do* work. The psychic healer is said to transfer energy to his patient. Demons are at work in all these areas. Then there are the energy-balancers we have looked at in this section of the alternative medicine guide. We are said to be energy around which matter is built. What we can see is supposedly not the reality; reality is found only through our 'higher self'! Although this is a false idea, it is demonstrable when consciousness is altered. It is the thinking prominent in eastern religions.

Experiences in altered states of consciousness through meditation, drugs, and these energy ideas, give rise to the idea that 'all is one'. Admittedly it is difficult for the mind to comprehend this sort of language describing occult experiences. One evening as a 'searcher' I spent many hours with a spiritualist medium. 'I am at one with that vase,' she told me, as she pointed to the porcelain on the mantle shelf. Slowly I came to understand her 'all is one' situation. The distinctions we recognise had disappeared for her. Another result of this new consciousness is the disappearance of the distinction between good and evil. New Age people aim to become aware of this divine nature, and against all that the Bible teaches. Their enlightenment, altered consciousness and experiences of spiritual power serve to show them they have succeeded.

Today many scientists are caught up in the occult explosion and their findings have to be increasingly regarded with great caution and discernment. Happily those scientists who are *not* caught up in it will not take these so-called energies very seriously.

New Age healing looks not to the Kingdom of God or to medical science, but to energies, forces, radiations, vibrations and the equivalent word in every false religion or occult therapy. The gospel of the New Age may be reduced to Satan's lies as given to Adam and Eve, 'You will be like God, and you will not die.' This idea of man as a divine being is being promoted in alternative medicine; Satan would subtly draw us from the idea of worshipping our Creator.

We are all in God's plan. We are known to Him as individuals. It is that way with Satan too. It makes little difference to Satan or to the patient if a well-meaning acupuncturist with his heart in the right place puts his needles in the wrong place. It makes no difference, and that is one of the ways new techniques are born! There are new ones all the time. One is *orthobionomy*. I received an impressive-looking certificate with a seal and a Californian name on it. My training lasted two days. With Satan on my side I didn't need even one day! It worked! I didn't know it but I was part of New Age medicine.

6: So-called psychological therapies

Foremost in the field of these therapies is *hypnotherapy*. This uses *hypnosis* which is increasingly accepted in the medical profession. Christians today are almost generally agreed that hypnotism opens the way for evil spirits. Indeed Emile Krémer has described it as the most effective way. His book *Eyes Opened to Satan's Subtlety* printed in seven languages, has the following to say about hypnosis:

> Serious damage to the soul is thereby done, quite apart from the fact that the patient's spirit is bound by hypnotic, spiritistic and occult powers. This ancient oriental art of suggestion and hypnotism, which is of demonic origin and has been used in magic and divination by the most ancient nations, has reappeared under the seemingly innocent cloak of 'modern science' and paves the way for similar modern methods of 'healing' and delusion. Through the complete elimination of will-power and of the conscious use of the senses, hypnotism is the most effective way of opening the door to all sorts of evil spirits.

Readily available, in some Health Food stores and advertised in many places, we find *self-hypnosis tapes* for use in our own cassette recorders. Favoured by large numbers who would not yet venture to a hypnotist, they are very dangerous. Let eyes be opened to Satan's subtlety! Once again we see the introduction of subliminal sounds to bring what the merchants describe as 'a

brilliant new concept in self-improvement and healing.'
Freud reckoned our subconscious controlled most of our
lives. The customers want their lives changed in one
way or another; the subliminal tapes, reaching into the
subconscious seem to provide the answer the easy way.
All that the conscious hears is the sound of the ocean or
the singing of birds!

'*The thief comes only to steal and kill and destroy; I have
come that they may have life, and have it to the full.*' (John
10:10). Satan wants us in a passive state whether this is
achieved through yoga, hypnosis or any other way.
When we abandon ourselves in these ways, Satan is given
an opportunity. He is a legalist and his demons are given
a right to oppress us. The particular technical method
used is less important than grasping the principle
involved.

Another method is *meditation*. When proficient, no
help will be needed from another in order to 'switch
off'. What we are describing here is the counterfeit of
Christian meditation, which is quite a different thing.
Meditation has been made well known by the Beatles.
They innocently provided the publicity for *transcendental
meditation* which is now a multi-million dollar business.
The effect of meditation is that the mind is emptied or
concentrated on something other than the mind of God.
It is opened up and demons take over. Meditation goes
beyond the thinking mind. It transcends it. Today there
are aids of every description – from mantras to moni-
toring devices – to speed meditators to higher levels of
consciousness.

For me, sophisticated electroencephelograph (EEG)
machines were used to encourage my progress to alpha
brainwave patterns and higher meditation states. Transcendental Meditation, or *TM* as it is most commonly
called, is very dangerous. For the Beatles, wasn't it the
next step after the drug scene, and do we not see a
parallel in medicine today? It was reported in May 1984
that there were doctors at one hospital who were

persuading patients that peace of mind through TM might be a better cure for their ills than their pills. It was argued that putting TM on prescription, and making it free under the National Health Service, could save hundreds of millions of pounds. It may not be long before the politicians see the economic possibilities in such a proposition!

Unless we keep our focus on Jesus, our hearts in the word of God as we read it in the Bible, and a balanced view of the Scriptures, Christians can be made to forget that Satan can masquerade as an angel of light. His plan will work for each one of us if we give him a chance. Satan is very subtle. He can begin with any truth. 'Focus on Jesus', he might even say!

I had to learn that Jesus was not just another Mantra. The month immediately prior to my conversion and immediately following the death of my fellow 'searcher', was spent in more searching. But now my search took me to look at the dangers of the occult healing methods I had been involved with. During that month, and prompted by a notice in the magazine of my local Anglican church, I attended a weekend retreat for *contemplative prayer*. This can be an ordinary part of the Christian way of prayer, but I didn't know Jesus, and the repetitive words and thoughts that were the basis of the time spent in the Retreat Chapel can, for me, only have been mantras. However what of the dangers generally with this kind of meditation? Mental passivity provides an open door for the enemy; free-will can diminish with the repetitiveness of whatever is said.

Autosuggestion is another therapy that doesn't need the participating help of another. *Couéism* involved the repetition of the words, 'Every day and in every way, I'm getting better and better.' *Visualisation therapy* is a variety of autosuggestion commonly found today, and used with cancer patients. They are asked to relax, focus on breathing, and to visualise or imagine the cancer under attack until it eventually disappears. Such imagination is the counterfeit of God's faith. From meditation and autosuggestion are developed other therapies. One is a method of *mind control* where there is an emphasis on expanding intuition and extra-sensory perception (ESP). It seems to be a sort of dynamic meditation. It is a counterfeit of listening to God's direction; also ESP is very dangerous – a power to be renounced and repented of by Christians if they find that they have it. Wherever and however the occult is involved, Satan is automatically given the right of access.

The use of *guided imagery* involves extending the meditative state to create a specific mental picture for diagnosis and healing. Carl Simonton, MD is an advocate of this mental imagery technique. In his book *Getting Well Again** he encourages patients to locate an 'inner guide'. We are to ask the guide's name, then ask it for help with our problems! It is true that we have natural healing mechanisms within us, but we are headed for danger when we start to see the subconscious as an infallible fountain of wisdom, or psychology (as the word is used today) as anything more than the science of the human soul and mind without God.

Chromotherapy is based upon the idea that every colour has a vibration rate different from that of any other colour. It is thousands of years old and there is a school of 'healers' using colour and music for healing.

Biofeedback describes the measurement of body changes – the sort we are not normally aware of – by using equipment. In the doctor's hands this can be quite legitimate, and the EEG machine for measuring brain-wave patterns is an example. The new application is in alternative medicine. Small versions of the EEG machine are available relatively inexpensively with a display panel so that the performance can be clearly seen. Meditators

* *Getting Well Again* by O. Carl Simonton MD, Stephanie Matthews-Simonton and James L. Creighton (Bantam Books, 666, Fifth Avenue, New York, NY 10103).

are encouraged to reach the so-called higher states of consciousness and trance previously only experienced by eastern gurus and holy men.

I used to sit, both in sessions with my guru and in my own office, wired up to the biofeedback equipment. Dave Hunt is an internationally recognised cult expert; his extensive research has taken him to over forty countries, and the following is how he sees the enormous significance of biofeedback in the context of what he calls New Age occult technology:

> Western technology has invented, designed, manufactured, and marketed, commercial devices for automatically producing the so-called 'higher' states of consciousness that open the door to occult experiences and psychic powers. What used to take a powerful dose of LSD or months of yoga meditation and vegetarianism can now be accomplished in a few minutes through new devices that are multiplying at an alarming rate. Biofeedback was one of the first such mechanisms. That those who developed it realised what they were doing is indicated by the fact that biofeedback is called 'electronic yoga.' The Menninger Clinic of Topeka, Kansas, has a promotional film titled 'Biofeedback, the Yoga of the West.' In other words biofeedback puts you in the same state of consciousness and develops the same control over involuntary bodily functions – and the same occult experiences and psychic powers – that have been the stock in trade of great Yogis since the Garden of Eden.*

With science on the side of the meditators, it is no longer necessary to spend half a lifetime in a yoga position

* Taken from *Peace, Prosperity & The Coming Holocaust*, copyright © 1983. Harvest House Publishers, 1075 Arrowsmith. Eugene. OR 97405, U.S.A. Used by permission.

staring into a fire in a Himalayan cave. The path to enlightenment, by way of the full awareness of all other Hindu beliefs, which we look at in Chapter Eleven, is much speeded up in these days.

I believe it will now be becoming clear that the traditional ways of Hinduism permeate alternative medicine. It will have its relevance in medical science too, but that is an area for separate study. However one therapy ought to be mentioned here, and that is the *placebo*. Studies show that large numbers of patients get better when given tablets known by the doctors to be useless, and these are called placebos. Is such faith well placed? Believe in it and it will work! Here we have the basis for a whole range of psychological pick-me-ups. It is true that many of these therapies, like the simple placebo, are not dangerous like TM or hypnosis. However, Christians will see many of them as poor attempts by man to organise God out of health care, and it is doubtful if much is achieved. Another psychological therapy in the field of alternative medicine is *autogenics*. This involves easy mental exercises to switch 'from the stress system to the rest, relaxation and recreation system.'

The therapies so far identified are solutions centred on 'self'. The 'self-realisation' of the higher states of consciousness of the east is similar to psychology's faith in such self-help techniques as go under the heading of *psychotherapy*. In his book, *Psychology as Religion*,* Paul Vitz, a Professor of Psychology, clearly presents psychology as the 'cult of self-worship'. Freud gave us *psychoanalysis*. This is a way of examining the soul! It involves a probing deep into the subconscious, thought life, imagination and unclean sexual dreams. The idea is one of discovery through an unhealthy method of looking inwards, and the search is for the cause of psychic and

---

* *Psychology as Religion – the Cult of Self Worship* by Paul C. Vitz (Lion) – 1977.

moral disorders. By ignoring or denying the relationship of sin and sickness, psychoanalysis hinders or destroys the healthy and biblical faith in Jesus. The mistake is the belief that wrongs can be put right if only we can discover ourselves. After Freud, Jung devoted himself to 'self-understanding' and 'self-realisation.' As with all psychology, reckoning man's behaviour apart from a knowledge of Jesus, these famous men have substantially failed in their task.

We find psychoanalysis at the root of techniques such as *dream therapy*. This is a group therapy where, one by one, the other members provide a commentary on the dream and where the dreamer can decide which, if any, fits!

In another psychological category, perhaps somewhat more acceptable, are the behavioural therapies such as *aversion therapy* where, for example, a drug given to an alcoholic is designed to make him sick if he drinks alcohol. However when we come to therapies grounded in humanistic psychology we find a minefield of danger. *Metamorphic technique* is based upon reflexology and works on points of the feet and elswhere that are supposed to relate to the nine-month cycle of prenatal growth. Another is *primal therapy*, or Rebirthing (discussed in Chapter Five). This seeks to discover problems arising from the time in the womb, using hypnotic age regression, psychedelics like LSD, simulation of the birth experience or breathing. *Inner healing*, as practised by Christians, has on occasions stumbled into this Satanic realm. In some forms of it self-discovery exercises and occult-related therapies more akin to the human potential movement are practised.

Rogerian therapy is said to be a path to 'self-actualisation' and trust in one's own inner growth. *Encounter therapy*, also to be avoided, is a development from this, emphasising physical expression. *Gestalt* is another with the aim of 'self-discovery' and 'self-liberation'. To throw off inhibitions there is *psychodrama* where problems can be acted out, and another therapy designed to uncover what we really feel is *transactional analysis*. Another is *co-counselling*, a recognised therapy where people help one another. *Clinical theology* is an approach promoted by the Clinical Theology Association. This exists for training people in counselling, and for the deepening of Christian life and growth towards personal maturity and stability. There is also provision in the Association's 'objects' for research 'into the integration of psychology and psychotherapy with the Christian faith.' Whilst the Association is an ecumenical Christian foundation, they do seem to believe not only in the respect for *people* with different beliefs (entirely right and proper according to Scripture), but also for personal convictions and religious heritages different from ours, as reflecting the freedom God gives to men and women. They regard the joint research of helper and the person seeking help, for firmer and deeper resources of meaning *within the counselee's own beliefs*, to be one of the important functions of counselling.

The Oxford Dictionary description of 'occult' is about the most useful I have seen: 'Kept secret, esoteric; recondite, mysterious, beyond the range of ordinary knowledge; involving the supernatural, mystical, magical.' As ever, the line is difficult to draw, but on any view it can be no part of my position to assert that the tools provided by transactional analysis and clinical theology qualify for that description. They are included because they involve therapies, as it were 'alternative' to what the doctor or psychiatrist might otherwise be called upon to provide. They are included also for the reason that Christians will sometimes turn from the 'drug' remedies, not only to the so-called 'natural' remedies, but also to the 'psychological'.

Clinical theology, founded by a psychiatrist in 1960, has always had good standing among church people. Transactional analysis was also originated by a psychiatrist, and in 1980 the Church of Scotland published *A Tool for Christians* to teach its use. The book described the subject in this way:

> Transactional Analysis is not 'Christian'. It is a secular theory of observable human behaviour and personality. It happens to be a theory which can be used within a Christian framework for it highlights much of what the New Testament teaches about human relationships. It is not a theology – it does not teach about God; but many of its insights can be of value to the modern Christian working out how to love his neighbour as himself.

Some will be helped to grow in their Christian life through transactional analysis, clinical theology, and other therapies that have their roots in psychology. However, we have to take care that we go God's way and not man's way. Psychology shifts us man's way; the Bible will take us God's way.

East meets west in the final categorisation of psychological therapy, *transpersonal psychology*. This is the psychology of 'transcendant experience', and therapists practising *psychosynthesis* attempt to harmonise the creation of a so-called healthy western-style personality with the eastern emphasis on higher levels of consciousness.

Emile Kremer★ tells us that *group dynamics* (or 'group therapy' or 'sensitivity training') has been rapidly spreading in the west for many years, not only in social, economic, scientific and political training centres but also in churches and Christian circles. There are groups under various names such as *group psychotherapy* and *interpersonal relationship*, as well as the encounter groups and transactional analysis mentioned previously. It is actually a form of 'brainwashing' and it is in some

★ *Eyes Opened to Satan's Subtlety* by Emile Kremer (M.O.V.E. Press 1969).

contrast to the Christian community where unity is through Jesus Christ and the focus of all upon him.

Born out of the ideas to be found in psychology, we hear much about *positive thinking* in relation to health. The Christian has a positive attitude, not because of his belief in the power there certainly is in positive thinking, but because he is trusting God. On the other hand the thinking of the human potential movement, advanced by many, can be identified in the Association of Humanistic Psychology. This is a world-wide network formed in 1962 for the development of the so-called human sciences in ways that recognise our human 'qualities' and which work towards fulfilling our 'innate' capacities. It explores human potential on the basis that it is infinite.

With *God* all things are possible. The *human potential movement* embracing many of the therapies in this chapter, takes the view, either that we don't *need* God, or that we *are* God. They believe that with *man* all things are possible. Indeed man is very powerful. Irrespective of what we believe in, we can make things happen by believing. The Christian way is quite different.

The *Daily Telegraph* reported (26 November 1984) that the teaching of fire-walking was coming to Britain: 'The other evening near Los Angeles she led a group of more than forty barefoot participants as they strode through an 8' pit of burning embers with a temperature of 1,300 degrees Fahrenheit. None suffered more than the odd blister.' It is Satanic. Some will be badly burned, but the price to be paid in the spiritual realm is even worse. Such is the human potential movement. While the world wonders, thank God for the discernment He gives to Christians on these things. Evidently there has been little 'scientific research' on this fire-walking! The article concludes: '. . . one theory holds that the feet have a cushion of surface moisture which vaporises to form an insulating cushion of steam for the very short duration of the walk'.

Like the voice of a departed relative or the ectoplasmic

manifestation of his or her body, this human potential is in one sense real enough. But the Christian should be able to recognise it as a counterfeit.

We have no worthwhile potential without Jesus. Indeed without Him we have a potential for Satan. Such is the guise of the human potential movement. The answer is in knowing both the character of God and the character of Satan.

7: Paranormal therapies

This is a description given by modern secular writers to the group of 'healing' therapies they can't understand in terms of pseudo-science, energy charts, astrology or whatever. We even see divine healing sometimes lumped in with the rest! The spiritually blind cannot see the difference between the real and the counterfeit.

Every occult method is dangerous and an undue categorisation of Satan's deceptions is undesirable. Also it isn't logical to go to great lengths comparing methods which anyway have their roots with spirits who are intentionally deceptive. However the broad headings of therapies in this part of the book will assist Christian understanding. While secular writers on 'alternative medicine' are separating the paranormal and the psychic from the rest and conceding 'we don't yet fully understand . . .', discerning Christians are identifying the spiritual however it is disguised.

It is clear that involvement with some of the paranormal therapies in this particular section brings the patient into contact with practitioners powerfully gripped by Satan.

Spiritualist healing is very dangerous indeed. Healing which is not God's, in the name of Jesus, is Satan's. Such healing is found in Spiritualist churches, in so-called Christian Spiritualist churches, and in some so-called Christian churches where the fellowship either doesn't know Jesus or where it is simply undiscerning. Satan is behind every variation that is to be found. Some call themselves *psychic healers*. Others style themselves as *faith healers*. Then there are *hand healers*. Often the same people engage in *absent healing*. Christians don't have to be present with a patient in order to pray for him; neither do the practitioners of the counterfeits when they engage in absent healing. One healing network spells out a procedure of self-visualisation, starting with the feet and moving on throughout the body. Perhaps hundreds or even thousands in this particular network are doing this at the same time each week. Then fifteen minutes later they all move into the 'Healing time' when they visualise all the others in the network sending them 'light' and 'love'! They bring into their imagination anyone they know who needs help and healing. They visualise them as filled with selfless love and light. The idea is that the more people there are in the group the better. They emphasise it has nothing to do with religion but that human beings are helping each other with love. According to the network, some call it 'spirit' and some call it 'synergy'. Whatever they call it, the source of any apparent healing is quite clear. They are opening themselves up to the activities of demons.

Another area where the hands are involved is *magnetic healing*. It has nothing to do with magnets. Yet one practitioner I have seen does use magnets for healing! There is a British Bio-magnetic Association which runs Seminars on *healing with magnets*.

Some healers go into trance or altered state of consciousness. They make contact with what they call 'spirit guides'. They either believe they are possessed by them or simply that the guides take over their movements and leave their minds clear. The 'Healer' may get verbal instructions from demons by clairaudience, or he may see the problem and its explanation by a sort of x-ray experience – clairvoyance. Given the diagnosis, the healing may be brought about by hand passes, or however the 'spirit' leads. Healers vary in their beliefs and techniques. Indeed the variety is a parallel counterfeit to the multiple methods of healing that Jesus used and which He uses today to bring about the manifestation of the good health that He suffered the bruises to bring us. Other healers in the spirit of the New Age movement, are interested in the so-called scientific explanation of the healing and they don't need to identify with any religious notion of a spirit guide.

Whatever the variations in description, I believe we can identify this sort of healing as psychic, coming from the 'psyche' (Gk. soul). The soul is made up of mind, will and emotions, and psychic healing comes from the mind rather than the spirit. The spirit of the Christian is occupied by the Holy Spirit, that same Holy Spirit that indwells all born again believers and which raised Jesus from the dead. Divine healing, looked at in scriptural detail in Part Five, involves the Holy Spirit.

The use of the term 'spiritual healing' or 'spiritualist healing' may imply that the spirit of the healer is taken over by, in this case, a demonic spirit. However 'faith healers', 'spiritual healers' and all the rest of them, usually using the laying on of hands, have often little to distinguish them. Clearly at one extreme there can be those powerfully possessed by demons. At the other extreme, we might find, even in the so-called charismatic fellowships of Bible-believing Christians, some that put the wrong emphasis on the 'psyche', where the Holy Spirit is absent and where there is no discernment as to the source of the power. If our faith is centred on Jesus and His word, if the occult is not involved, and if the healing is in the name of Jesus, by people who know Jesus, then we should have nothing to fear.

What of *psychic surgery*? Many wonder if it is an illusion when the psychic surgeon in Mexico uses a dirty knife to open up a patient's body, and when the wound immediately is sealed at the close of an operation during which extraordinary foreign bodies have been removed; or when, in the Philippines, the patient's body is opened up, in the view of qualified medical investigators, with no cutting instruments used. It is *not* an illusion. It is *not* nonsense. In these days too, even western man is seeking out the 'genuine' *witchdoctor* or *shaman*. In Satan's plan the witch still curses and the witchdoctor, as the name implies, still 'heals'.

Our own pagan practices, like the *charming of warts* and *copper bracelets* for rheumatism, must also be renounced by Christians. Another self-healing method is with crystals, and no doubt it can be fairly described as *crystal therapy!* One practitioner teaches that we should sit quietly, then focus on places of pain and tension in the body. Next we place a crystal we 'feel attracted to', either directly on the place that needs it, or in the left hand, 'allowing the left hand to place the crystal "intuitively" on the part of the body that needs it.' He continues, 'At the "Crystal Explorer Groups" currently held twice weekly . . . one can go far deeper, with loving support, into crystal energies.' We can put our faith in anything in order to get results! *Pattern therapy* assumes patterns or shapes can help cure disease. The same goes for *pyramid healing*. Pyramid power was important to the pharaohs, and occultists use it today.

Ayurveda from India is perhaps the oldest medical discipline. It is rooted in the occult. The Greeks picked up aspects of it, and much of our own medicine came from Greece. As for India, ayurveda is still responsible for most health care in that country today. It is endorsed by the World Health Organisation, and ayurvedic medicine now has its own association in Britain.

Therapeutic touch, found in a whole range of practitioners in these days, is a good example of the ancient energy concept of 'prana' dressed for acceptibility today. It is even taught to some nurses. It is listed here in the 'paranormal' section since arm waving around the body, without any touch at all, is quite common in this therapy. It is a therapy most readily grasped by those who have looked in on yoga or the martial arts. *Applied kinesiology* is optional teaching in some chiropractic training schools and 'touch for health', referred to in Chapter Five is a well known therapy under this heading. Once again touch may not be touch at all. Directing to the so-called aura or etheric body, some will simply make a hand pass and wave it close to the skin.

Derived from applied kinesiology is *behavioural kinesiology*. This attempts to demonstrate with a so-called 'arm strength test', how food, clothes, art and various other factors cause fluctuations in 'life energy'. Names! Names! In Satan's plan, the more the better. 'Bio' prefixes much in science and medicine, and so it is also in occult medicine! One treatment described to me was called *biokinesiology*. The idea was to identify dietary substances which would be harmful to the patient. Small amounts of the substance under test were in turn placed upon the subject's tongue whilst the practitioner attempted to lower the subject's arm as it was held extended first above the head, then about waist level, and then lower. Apparently it was quite easy for the subject to resist these attempts to move his arm, except when any dietary substance 'harmful' to him was placed upon his tongue when he seemed powerless to resist the force applied by the practitioner. Then a similar procedure was repeated, but this time instead of the substance being placed on the tongue they remained in their unopened bottle and the bottle was placed on the skin of the abdomen. This had the same apparent effect on muscle power, and the harmful substances thus identified were the same in both instances – fish, tea, sugar and monosodium glutamate.

Neurologists properly tell us that muscle power in the same individual will vary and depend most of all on his *will* to resist. It is also true that we once again have the deception of that common denominator found in so much of the paranormal – 'energy'. The word biokinesiology is derived from 'kinetic' (energy; Gk. 'kinetikos') but it is a counterfeit; for it to be otherwise, as one

Christian writer* on this has put it, it seems every textbook on physiology would have to be rewritten.

The spiritual healing to be found in *Christian Science* is neither Christian nor scientific and has to be avoided. Satan will sometimes heal through Christian Science. He is the source of sickness and he can certainly take away the symptoms to accomodate the cultists and get a better hold on the gullible. Satan always has a high price – mental breakdown, suicide, oppression, etc.

Finally I introduce to you *past lives therapy!* Patients are asked by the therapist to recreate scenes in past lives for the supposed purpose of understanding the present problems. It is a Satanic deception, and of course the evil one can also provide the scenes.

These paranormal therapies have, in one subtle way and another, introduced through alternative medicine numerous aspects of Hindu doctrine set up by Satan to deceive us. Yet to some of us, past lives therapy isn't really that subtle! Satan would like us to forget any idea of hell as he advertises a 'next life' after this one. The idea is prompted just as well by the concept of a 'past life!' The view that we are indeed in the last of the last days is supported by the way that these more blatant lies are received by the intelligent. More and more are being deceived, Christian and non-Christian alike.

* *The Holistic Healers* by Paul C. Reisser, M.D., Teri K. Reisser and John Weldon. Inter Varsity Press, Downers Grove, Illinois 60515, U.S.A. (1983).

8: Paranormal diagnosis

In the field of *psychic diagnosis* the foremost figure was Edgar Cayce. His trance states provided very accurate diagnosis. Psychics can be very accurate today and they are more and more consulted by doctors who are themselves deceived. To be a receiver of treatment following this diagnosis is not to be distant from Satan's influence. Any sort of involvement with the methods of Satan, either directly or indirectly, intentionally or not, is very dangerous.

Radiesthesia is a pseudo-scientific term meaning the perception of radiations which are said to emanate from everything that exists. Some are into this invisible world without needing a pendulum or other device. They see by *clairvoyance* or hear by *clairaudience*. Deceiving spirits answer the enquirer, and those already opened up through superstitions, charming or other occult practices are sometimes able to progress quickly in these counterfeit gifts. Often these gifts come down a family line. The Bible says that sins are visited on future generations, and children who have received *inherited powers* will retain them until they are renounced and repented. Typically a *pendulum* is used in diagnosis. For example, when I moved my pendulum down the spinal cord of one of my subjects, a swing in the reverse direction would be expected where the problem was located and the energy out of balance. Once again results are ascribed to energy or radiations without any attempt to describe their nature or prove their existence. The same explanations are given for water divining (or 'water witching' or 'water dowsing'); but when asked to explain the success at dowsing from maps, practitioners are forced to abandon this reasoning.

For the mechanically minded, radiesthesia can become *radionics*. Human hair or some other body element is shown to the machine! A modern-day encyclopaedia of 'natural health and healing' describes the apparatus as using the thought of the skilled operator as a probe in determining the basic causes of ill-health. What next! Some of these modern-day diviners will use *psychometry*. This involves giving a body sample, again hair or anything else, to a perhaps absent practitioner.

Kirlian photography can show the Kirlian practitioner a photographed aura of his patient. This is the halo effect said to represent the etheric body and is akin to the aura that many psychics can see around the human body. They really do see these auras. Like poltergeists, they are manifestations to further the purpose of keeping man away from God. The Kirlian photograph is made of the fingers, and the interpretation is based upon the patterns and colours in the photograph. It is a modern version of *palmistry*, itself occult, and still used for diagnosis. *Mediumistic iridology* (or 'eye diagnosis'), using the eye rather like a crystal ball, is another source for diagnosis used by therapists with half-baked scientific ideas and spiritually deceived.

Astrologic medicine is a form of divination based on the belief that signs – in this case of the sun, moon and planets in the lines of the zodiac – correspond to lines of physical, mental, emotional and spiritual well-being. Astronomy is a science; astrology is occult. *Biorhythms* is another deception increasingly looked at by alternative practitioners. It holds that there are three body cycles (physical – 23 days; emotional – 28 days; intellectual – 33 days) running from birth to death. The idea is to know when to avoid stressful occasions and potential illness. Its charts, like those in astrology, are for the curious and seem to have no basis in science.

Whilst some psychics do not need a pendulum or any

sort of equipment at all, the world takes time examining the equipment! Doctors take time examining the results! There even exists the Psionic Medicine Society. An additional professional qualification is offered to doctors and dentists by the Institute of Psionic Medicine. This extension of the medical profession seems to offer an integrated system linking orthodox medicine, homoeopathy and radiesthesia. It is all relatively new. The Society was formed in 1968. Except on the basis of 'It doesn't work!', like so much in alternative medicine, it seems to go substantially unchallenged by the medical profession.

9: Homoeopathy

This is a branch of medicine based on herbs and minerals. It uses highly diluted solutions said to become more powerful the greater the dilution. The power of the solution is further believed to depend upon shaking to release the drug's energy. There appears to be no accepted scientific base for Hahnemann's application of these ideas. (Hahnemann was the founder of homoeopathy).

Homoeopathy arrived in Britain around 1840. It was introduced by a Dr Quin who is said to have had influential friends. Eventually the London Homoeopathic Hospital acquired its 'Royal' status. Sir John Weir was appointed personal physician and served four monarchs for forty-eight years until 1971. There is still a homoeopathic physician serving the Royal Family today and most homoeopathic doctors are believed to acknowledge that the Royal Family has helped to keep homoeopathy alive in Britain.

Homoeopathy is thus established in the ranks of a medical profession dominated by the question: 'does it work?' While answers are being sought to that question (both in this and other areas of counterfeit healing) the spiritual aspect continues to be missed. Satan smiles!

Hahnemann was deceived. After 150 years man still hasn't found his scientific answer, and the deception has continued. Satan has blinded to the truth of it. It thrives in India! In Britain it survives! By and large doctors don't like what they see as an absence of science; but it is much worse than that!

Personal testimony

Before any so-called intellectual approach, God spoke to me in this way.

Attending a Christian conference, a friend pointed out a Christian doctor to me. 'He's a homoeopathic doctor', I was told much to my surprise. It seemed to be a nudge from God for, just an hour before, in another place, I had also been taken aback.

En route to the conference I had thumbed through a new Christian exposé on psychic healing.* Homoeopathy had been lumped in with what were described as 'fascinatingly named healing alternatives'. There they were – iridology, astrologic medicine, colour therapy, sound therapy, radionics, kinesiology, orgonomy, biofeedback, 'past lives' therapy, zone therapy, rolfing, polarity therapy, Kirlian photography, to name just a few. I had been involved with some of them; they were occult. I had given some of them a miss but I knew they were occult. Some I sensed were occult, but I didn't know for sure. Homoeopathy, although not among those the author singled out as positively occult (I later learned he hadn't yet researched it fully), had seemed to be the odd man out.

I had passed the Bristol Homoeopathic Hospital every day on my way to the university. Very respectable it had all seemed. So I was surprised by the book, and just an hour later – after reading it and now sitting in the conference hall – it seemed God was directing me to a Christian homoeopathic doctor.

My friend gave me the doctor's name and address. Was God telling me that homoeopathy was not of Him? Or was he telling me to seek the advice of the Christian homoeopathic doctor? I knew that people involved in the occult could not be good witnesses, Christian or not.

* *Psychic Healing – an exposé of an occult phenomenon* by John Weldon and Zola Levitt (Moody Press, Chicago, USA) 1982.

It was no time to consult the doctor! I waited upon the Lord.

Several months passed. Although living a good distance from the doctor, circumstances brought us together and we came to know one another on a continuing basis. I shared my concern about homoeopathy with him. 'Homoeopathy is certainly of God', he assured me. It was time to wait upon the Lord once again.

More months passed. I was seated outside a café in Brussels. A young Dutch Christian, whom I didn't know, came and sat beside me. Somehow the subject of homoeopathy – not in my thoughts for a long time – came into the conversation. He gave me what at the time seemed the most extraordinary reason why he went to medical school. He wanted to get to the bottom of a whole area of occult medicine that included Paracelsus and homoeopathy. To me the explanations were very technical, but it seemed clear he had succeeded. He had done the research. Although I didn't understand fully, I was quite clear in my spirit, as he was in his, that homoeopathy was indeed occult.

Two days later, and back at home, an evangelist moved in with us for a few days. In the days immediately before (while I was learning from my new Dutch friend) she had been staying with the homoeopathic doctor who, by this time, had become a good friend of mine. The visitor to our home brought good news. She had discerned the spirit of homoeopathy. More than that, the Lord had spoken at the same time to my good friend. She told me he had renounced homoeopathy. He had destroyed the equipment and his homoeopathic medicines.

Homoeopathy (and not just the occult practices that sometimes accompany it) is from deceiving spirits.

The testimonies of others

Since the date of my own testimony, I have received testimonies from others. The following was written by a Christian doctor:

> In the experience of many patients, and overtly in various TV programmes on homoeopathy, the pendulum is being used; definitely an occult practice. Moreover, in our experience several Spirit-filled patients have not 'benefited' from homoeopathy but have actually had severe and damaging reactions to the treatment and their condition has deteriorated – remarkable considering that physically there is probably only sugar and water in the medication. (Testimonies can be given).
> We have also found that involvement with Homoeopathy has been one of the factors in preventing people from moving forward in their relationship with God, into the fullness of the Holy Spirit, and their new inheritance in Christ Jesus (Mark 16:17–18; Rom.8:14–17).

She concludes by saying that homoeopathy itself (and as well as the pendulum) is something for which repentance is necessary. It has to be renounced, like all occult therapies, whenever there has been involvement.

Treating the whole person

Homoeopathy has the aim that it seeks to treat the patient as a whole; an attraction shared with the ayurvedic doctor and a counterfeit of what Jesus died to provide – a so called 'holistic' medicine rather than authentic wholeness.

It has success with patients because it is presented as a treatment that is both personal and scientific, with a remedy both individual and natural. Patients seem readily to receive it in that way. Faced with the routines and mysteries that are in medical science also, patients are tempted to flit from one doctor to another without finding real help; then they find the homoeopath and the holistic approach. Usually they don't know that what they have found is a counterfeit.

One of the happy consequences of the First Edition of this book has been the growth in awareness of the dangers of homoeopathy. This has been evident from the correspondence and comment both here and in the United States.

Homoeopathy seems to be gaining ground along with most of the other alternative medicines. The so-called advantage of the homoeopathic doctor giving more time to the patient than his orthodox counterpart continues to be an important factor. However, on a less personal note, one firm is offering homoeopathic computers with a repertory of 9,000 symptoms and over 500 classical remedies!

Christians, however are on their guard! So far as I am aware, the first book published in the English language, dealing with both the scientific evaluation and the occult connection, was published in 1984. It is *Homeopathy* by H J Bopp MD, of Neuchatel, Switzerland, and he encourages the Christian, seeking to walk in the light and in obedience to his Lord, not to allow himself to be seduced by every brand of the 'in' philosophy and practice, especially when it comes to finding help for his body, the temple of the Holy Spirit (1 Cor. 6:19). That is why it is so important to look at the history, doctrinal origins and basis of homoeopathy.

History

In the classic study of magic and religion which first appeared in 1890, Sir James Frazer, FRS, FBA, analysed the principles of thought on which magic is based and concluded that broadly there were two principles. His

971–page volume* identifies the principle that things which have once been in contact with each other continue to act on each other at a distance after the physical contact has been severed. The second principle is that like produces like, or that an effect resembles its cause. Frazer calls this homoeopathic or imitative magic, and shows how the real thing can be affected by the imitation. He cites what is perhaps the best-known example of this principle: 'Perhaps the most familiar application of the principle that like produces like is the attempt which has been made by many peoples in many ages to injure or destroy an enemy by injuring or destroying an image of him, in the belief that, just as the image suffers, so does the man, and that when it perishes he must die.' In other words it is a principle of homoeopathic magic that you don't deal with the real, whether the enemy or the disease, but introduce something like it.

Disease is our enemy today, and it was Paracelsus in the sixteenth century who was the first to bring mystical research into the area of medicine. He sought to overthrow the classical idea of treating with opposites, with us since Galen (138–201 A.D.) and still the basis of orthodox medicine today. The ideas of Paracelsus were picked up 300 years later by Samuel Hahnemann, the founder of homoeopathy such as it is practised today. According to the French encyclopedia *Larousse du XXe siecle* (1930) he was believed to have received it through the 'revelation of heavenly powers.'

Doctrine in homoeopathy

In 1810 Hahnemann published what is still today the basis for all homoeopathic treatment: *Organ of the Art of Healing*. This marked a total break with classical and

* *The Golden Bough: A study in Magic & Religion* by J G Frazer (MacMillan & Co) – 1960.

orthodox medicine. The Montreux International Congress on Homoeopathy in 1960 celebrated the 150th anniversary of the *Organ*, and the nostalgia of the event provided the opportunity to see the up-to-date doctrinal views of homoeopathic doctors put on the record. The organiser summed up the *Organ* with these words: 'The *Organ* is for the homoeopath what the Bible is for the Christian. Homoeopathy must consider the *Organ* as the foundation and basis of its therapy.' Dr Bopp writes that Hahnemann's disciples are encouraged to meditate on the book, paragraph by paragraph, in order to grasp the spirit of it. Dr J Kunzil confirms this:

> You all know that today we are witnessing a reinstatement and new progressive emergence of homoeopathy in many countries. This entire movement will only lead to results on condition that it draws its strength exclusively from the *Organ*. . . . A dry, historical and theoretical study will serve no purpose and will bring no help to your patients. You've got to penetrate the spirit of this remarkable book; you must reflect and meditate on all it contains, and the more you study it, the greater will be the profit you'll derive from it.*

The President of the International League on Homoeopathy, a doctor from Rome, chose words at the Montreux Congress that make the position clear to a discerning Christian: 'It's futile to reject this or that principle enunciated in the *Organ*. There remains more than enough to recognise the unfathomable intuition and divinatory spirit of its author.

Hahnemann and the *Organ*

The picture of Hahnemann presented by Trevor Cook in his biography *Samuel Hahnemann* is that of a religious

* *Swiss Periodical Journal on Homoeopathy* – No 2 / 1962.

freethinker, decidedly deistic rather than Christian, and a freemason. He was described as a godly man, at least according to the traditions of his day. He practised mesmerism, a kind of hypnosis assumed by Mesmer to be based upon the occult radiation of power.

Hahnemann placed on the title page of his *Organ* the words *aude sapere* (dare to be wise) the freemasonry motto.

In the *Organ* we read: 'A person becomes ill when a diseased agent infiltrates the body and disturbs the vital energy by dynamistic influence.' So what is this 'vital energy'? Man is body, soul (mind, will and emotions) and spirit. Hahnemann's concept of spirit was this 'vital energy', the Hindu 'prana'. Like so many therapies in this area of alternative medicine, homoeopathy is a spiritual treatment, and accordingly the cure is applied *to* this vital energy. Also the law of similarity (or homoeopathic magic) provided for in the *Organ* means that the cure must resemble the disease as closely as possible in the totality of its symptoms when tested on a healthy man. The *Organ* states: 'All homoeopathic medicines cure illnesses the symptoms of which they most resemble.'

The *Organ* has this to say about this 'immaterial energy' or 'vital energy': 'The doctor can only remove these morbid affections (illnesses) by bringing to bear on this immaterial energy certain substances endowed with modifying properties that are equally immaterial (dynamic) and are discerned by the all-pervasive nervous system. Accordingly it's only by their dynamic action on the vital energy that the curative remedies are able to redress and do indeed redress the biological balance and restore health.'

The 'prana' of yogic philosophy, the 'innate' energy described by Palmer, the founder of chiropractic, the 'ch'i' from China, the 'force' that many traditions see as God, and the 'vital energy' of the homoeopathic doctors; are they not all pure deception? On from homoeopathy, Rudolf Steiner took the same concept and gave us anthroposophical treatments. They are generally homoeopathic containing the same occult force.

Of course those who see some sort of scientific or even natural energy at work in water divining, or who believe that water divination is a gift from God, will perhaps have some difficulty in seeing the evil that is at work in homoeopathy.

Power through diluting and shaking

Homoeopathic preparations may be sweetened or given a taste, but diluting and shaking using quite ordinary water is the essence of the idea. The teaching is that the more diluted the substance, the more powerful it is. Dilution is measured according to a scale from CH 1 to CH 100 or more, and each of the dilutions from 1 to 100 is made according to one drop of the previous dilution plus ninety-nine drops of water or liquid. Dr Bopp tells us that

. . . any patient receiving a homoeopathic treatment at CH 30 should be under no illusions as to its composition. There is no longer any material substance in the pill or liquid whatsoever. However, such mathematical proof doesn't in the least upset the homoeopathic doctors. Their teaching declares that the more diluted the substance, the more active it is. It's not just a question – and this is their secret – of a simple dilution, but of a process known as dynamisation or potentialisation, produced by repeatedly shaking the mixture between dilutions. Such repeated concussion makes it possible to contact and retain a hidden power in the liquid, its immaterial essence.

What about vaccination?

To the layman, vaccination and homoeopathy may seem to have much in common. Dr Bopp explains that in fact vaccination is quite different: 'Vaccination immunises an individual against a microbal disease by inoculating him with the attenuated microbe or its toxin. The technique is well known, clearly defined. It consists of stimulating the production of specific antibodies to act against the microbe. Homoeopathy is not based on this technique. There is no production of specific antibodies.'

All homoeopathy is dangerous

Satan's lie is at the heart of all that is occult, and it is clearly seen in homoeopathy. As Dr Bopp puts it, the predominant strain of pantheism would place God everywhere, in each person, each animal, plant, flower, cell, and even in homoeopathic medicine. One homoeopathic doctor saw the role of his medicament in this way: 'The cure alone really knows the patient, better than the doctor, better than the patient himself. It knows just where to locate the originating cause of the disorder and the method of getting to it. Neither the patient nor the doctor has much wisdom or knowledge.' The doctor is really saying that the medicament has become a god.

Despite the fact that many Christians are being deceived and are turning from drugs to homoeopathy, it is another counterfeit – subtle, powerful and rooted in the occult. There can be no half measures. *All* homoeopathic and anthroposophical treatments have to be avoided.

Dr Bopp's conclusion, which could be applied with some slight variation to the great majority of therapies in this book, is as follows:

. . . the occult influence, by nature hidden,
disguised, often dissimulated behind a parascientific
theory, does not disappear and does not happen to
be rendered harmless by the mere fact of a
superficial approach contenting itself simply with
denying its existence. HOMOEOPATHY IS

DANGEROUS. It is quite contrary to the teaching of the Word of God. It willingly favours healing through substances made dynamic, that is to say, charged with occult forces. Homoeopathic treatment is the fruit of a philosophy and religion that are at the same time Hinduistic, pantheistic and esoteric. . . . Contact with immaterial essence, the invisible force of the ethereal world operative in the medicament, sullies the Christian. The occult influence in homoeopathy is transmitted to the individual, bringing him consciously or unconsciously under demonic influence. Very often the result is a bond with Satan. A person may be cured of a bodily ailment . . . but spiritual life ebbs away. In this very connection it is significant frequently to find nervous depression in families using homoeopathic treatments.

Christians must not allow themselves to be seduced by the fact that homoeopathy can effect remarkable cures. It's not a question of denying them, even if scientific medicine lacks the explanations. The Bible teaches us that Satan, through the agency of men, is capable of performing miracles and healings. *'For false Christs and false prophets will appear and perform great signs and miracles to deceive even the elect – if that were possible.'* (Matthew 24:24) The sense of the Greek here is that it is indeed possible!

10: Cults and the occult – a checklist

God's word in Deuteronomy (18:9–14) and in other Scriptures, forbids involvement in the occult realm. The answer to involvement is in renunciation, repentance and faith in Jesus Christ and His atoning blood. The help of Bible-believing, born again Christians, filled with the Holy Spirit, is also needed by those deeply affected. Through them the powers of Satan can be rebuked and deliverance claimed for them in the name of Jesus.

Before release will come it is often necessary for Christians to pray in the name of Jesus that the Holy Spirit will bring to their minds an honest and truthful recollection of past occult involvements. The names of therapies highlighted in the previous chapters may serve as reminders for this.

The checklist that follows includes broad areas of cults and the occult. They are arranged in no significant order and the names are once again intended to assist in the recall of past involvement. Some areas are covered more than once where different names are used. Some are already referenced in the body of the book as alternative medicine therapies. Others are difficult to categorise in one section or another. However they can all have a common source and there can be an occult element with each of them. Some of the items listed will have a harmless or even Christian application. An example is the sort of 'handwriting analysis' used by the police; this is perfectly acceptable. Another that is listed is 'exorcism'. This is another word for deliverance; the counterfeit of Christian deliverance or exorcism is practised by some who use occult power.

The list is not intended as a basis for further research or to throw at unsuspecting Christians unfamiliar with the sort of message that is central in this book. We have all of us, in some measure, been open to some of Satan's wiles. The Holy Spirit will be the communicator and if He can use this list to prompt a reminder of a past involvement that needs renouncing, then it will have served its purpose. Frequently too, the mention of one area can prompt the recall of others not listed or described in the same way.

The Bible tells us (Exodus 20:5; Deuteronomy 23:2, etc) that the sins of our fathers are carried through to future generations. The checklist can serve to remind of any known involvements by past or present members of the family. It is right to renounce our involvement no matter how innocently, even once, and at whatever age. Satan is no respecter of age or of persons. We are born sinners and Satan knows it! We need to consider if at any time we were present when things listed were going on. In these days it is also necessary to consider our openness to occult areas through radio and TV as well as through books, school, films, etc. There is no need to struggle and agonise over what is after all, a formidable list. As we look carefully through, we can trust the Holy Spirit to bring recall if we approach it in a prayerful way from the heart; also God can give discernment to others for us.

Occult

Hatha Yoga	Magic (black & white)
Cartomancy	Reincarnation
Fortune telling	Spiritism
Palmistry	Tarot cards
Charms	Spells
Birth signs	Hypnosis
Pentagrams	Osiris
Ouija boards	'Dungeons and Dragons'
Levitation	Astral travel

Automatic writing
Clairvoyance
Clairaudience
Divination
Telepathy
Superstitions
Mind control
Psychic powers
Pendulum swinging
Table tipping
Handwriting analysis
Hallowe'en
Akashic records
Almanac
Age of Aquarius
Aquarian gospel
Soul travel
Horoscopes
Atlantis
Aura
Taboos
Amulets
Dream interpretation
Exorcism
ESP
Rudolf Steiner
Intuitive arts counselling
Phrenology
Card cutting
Hand reading
Teacup reading
Rod divination
Seances
Martial arts
Judo
Ju-jitsu
Ch'uan-fa
Kung-fu

Taekwondo
Taoism
Mushindo karate
Aikido
T'ai Chi Ch'uan
Karate
Hapkido
Wu Shu
Spirit combat
Feng-sao
Dowsing
Soothsayers
Augury
Automatic drawing
Devil dancing
Fetishes
Firewalking
Hexagrams
Omens
Telekinesis
Mesmerism
Autosuggestion
Cabbala
Mascots
Numerology
Incantations
Talismans
Fantasy role-playing
 games
Card reading
Psychoanalysis
Freud
'Holy' objects
AMORC
Oriental ornaments
Addictions
Spoon bending
Voices in the mind

Standing stones
Ley lines
Religious idols
Church pagan connections
Graphology
Incubus
Succubus
Parapsychology
Psycho-cybernetics
UFO's
Yoga
Charming
Curses (*by* you or *on* you)
Lucky charms
Kabala
Tribal dancing
Astral projection
Candle staring
Drugs
Ghosts
Pagan celebrations
Gipsy curse
Psychokinesis (PK)
Zodiac signs
I Ching

Evil eye
Electric shock treatment
Nanbudo
Water divining
Mirror mantic
Kissing of idols
Glass moving
Idols
Teraphims
Stargazing
Old Moore
Stonehenge
Demonised souvenirs
Buddhas
Swastika
Images (frogs, cats, owls,
    bats and night creatures
    used in witchcraft)
Indian elephants
Pyramids
Obelisks
Serpents
Witch markings
Myths
Fairies and pixies

Cults
Anglo-Israelism
The Worldwide Church
    of God
Baha'ism
Black Muslims
Christian Science
Conceptology
Freemasons and other
    secret societies
I AM
Inner Peace Movement

Jehovah's Witnesses
Modernism, liberalism
    and the social gospel
Mormonism
New thought
Rosicrucianism
Satanism
Scientology
Seventh Day Adventism
Spiritual Frontiers
    Fellowship

Spiritualism
Swedenborgianism
Theosophical Society
Unitarianism
Unity School of
  Christianity
Universalism
Ultimate reconciliation
Voodoo
Witchcraft
Zen Buddhism
Marxism
Moral Rearmament
Astrology
Human Potential
  Movement
Children of God
Hare Krishna
Gurdjieff
Baba-lovers
Sufi
Transcendental
  Meditation
Divine Light Mission
Christadelphianism
The Healing Movement
Cooneyites
False religions
Druids

Communism
Buffaloes
Islam (Mohammedism)
Hinduism
Buddhism
Humanism
Eastern ceremonial dances
Pagan customs
Shrines
Pagan tourist places
Subud
Shepherding/Discipleship
Moonies
Unification Church
Anthroposophy
'Star Wars'
Theosophy
False philosophies
Belief systems
Mary worship
Eckankar
Est
The Way
Personal growth movement
Mind dynamics
Erhard Seminars Training
The Aquarian Gospel
Zoroastrianism
Family of Love

That is a formidable list of areas that *can*, in one way or another, open the way for Satan. Let us not take a wholly intellectual viewpoint and trouble ourselves unduly about whether a particular area is properly defined there as a cult or as occult. Items could have been omitted in order to satisfy the intellectual mind! However I believe this would have made the list less useful. In the same way, we could carry on listing more areas of opportunity for Satan and where we have to take note of his possible wiles; but where do we draw the line? A serious illness? A major operation? Severe emotional shock? A coma? A car accident? A difficult birth? A miscarriage? Like many on the checklist, these things are often totally outside our control. However, and without fitting in any way into the heading of 'occult', they can still present real opportunity for demonic activity to project negativism and perhaps more serious bondages.

11: Sorting out the alternatives!

Language fails!

I have tried to slot each therapy into a broad category (physical, psychological and paranormal therapies, and paranormal diagnosis). I have tried in the last chapter to separate the cults and the occult. The distinctions are necessarily broad ones. When we look at therapies that emphasise the occult and therapies that emphasise psychology or a misplaced faith, we once again find difficulty. There is no clear dividing line. Christians will accept or reject a therapy for themselves according to the leading of the Holy Spirit.

At one end of the danger scale, spiritual healing is occult and mightily dangerous, as I learned through my own experience. It is forbidden according to God's word. At the other end of the scale there are the innocuous treatments; Christians can teach that God's way, looked at in Chapter Twenty-two is even better. In between, we find therapies like homoeopathy, discussed in Chapter Nine. Apart from its root in the occult we have seen that its power is based upon the deception of energy passing from the herb or mineral into the water, in line with traditional Hindu beliefs. Also in homoeopathy there is room for the 'faith' element, of the placebo kind, that will help the success of the treatment along in the same way that many orthodox drugs are made more effective. Not so obviously perilous, but quite unlike the kind of faith we can receive from God, and unlike the leaves provided for our healing (Ezekiel 47:12), are those therapies involving a faith in some fantasy that has no basis in scripture or in science. The inert placebo* is the best example.

Our relationship with Jesus starts with our coming to Him and receiving Him in *faith* (John 1:12). Our walk with Jesus is a walk in faith. '*Faith comes from hearing the message, and the message is heard through the word of Christ.*' (Romans 10:17) The sort of faith we *actually* have is mirrored either by the depth of our descent into Satan's kingdom or by the heights to which we trust God to lead us. Jesus can meet all our health and healing needs. We can receive from Him as we get more and more revelation of the truth that is in Scripture.

Language cannot easily describe divine healing, simple though it is, to a disbelieving world. The same is often true when it comes to explaining occult alternative medicine, even to a Christian. I have walked with Satan into meditation, yoga, spiritual healing, divination with the pendulum, biofeedback, and more besides. I have walked with God in the power of the Holy Spirit. These are two different realms, one is the counterfeit of the other, but both are in a dimension different to the one the world knows. Language fails, but the truth is in God's supernatural word – the Bible.

In looking at alternative medicine we have to beware the irrelevant questions. On the world's view, any question is a fair question. We can sometimes be taken by a skilled debater to a point where we are cornered. Language is an even greater problem when we describe the spiritual dimension. Satan is a master with words and he can deceive us with them. Given an opportunity, he will work through our intellect. 'This therapy is really only for relaxation, isn't it?'; 'Now you're not really

---

* The 'inert' placebo can be something like a sugar pill that can have no medical effect. However doctors usually prescribe what might well be called the 'deceptive' placebo – a pill designed to perform some function, albeit irrelevant to the patient's need.

worshipping me when you're only doing it for exercise, are you?'; 'Oh, we both know Charlie well. You're not suggesting he's not really a Christian, are you?'; 'What's the harm in meditation; Christians do it, don't they?'; '*You will not surely die, for God knows that when you eat of it your eyes will be opened, and you will be like God, knowing good and evil.*' (Genesis 3:4–5)

The Bible tells us that Satan only comes to kill and steal and destroy, and in the Garden of Eden the serpent stole from Eve the truth of God's word. It has been happening ever since. The serpent's lie was subtle and complex in the garden. It is subtle and complex in Hinduism, and that subtlety is perceivable in the same way in alternative medicine. Hinduism is not against any other religion. Alternative medicine and its practitioners are not against any other form of medical treatment. They focus directly on the question, 'Does it work?', mostly blissfully unaware of Satan masquerading as an angel of light.

The language of Hinduism

All is one! The natural; the supernatural; Satan; God; man; animals; the earth; life; death; the Creator; the creation. The Hindu sees the whole physical world, including sickness and health, as an illusion (maya). Is it surprising that the value placed upon life is so low in the Hindu lands? The Hindu sees everything as a unity developing through 'evolution' to 'enlightenment'. The idea of evolution was essential to Hinduism long before Darwin came along and grabbed the limelight. Indeed, evolution ideas were essential to Hinduism *and* Buddhism; also to Taoism which is a blend of these with Confucianism, and more, added. The Hindu doctrines added together promote the lie that man is God who doesn't need salvation from his sin. I myself had a guru (a Hindu spiritual teacher). I so trusted him that no objective argument could have pulled me from the path to the 'enlightenment' he was bringing me into.

Biofeedback was the principal tool I used as I learned from my guru. Once I accepted that the altered state of consciousness I was reaching was 'higher', I came to see the everyday experiences of life as being 'lower', nothing but maya compared to the real experiences I had come into, and the enlightenment I had started to look forward to. I didn't know this was all deception. I didn't sit around philosophising either! I was above all that, and 'experience' was the great thing! Really, I was enjoying the experiences. I didn't know the intellectual explanations. I didn't know that my eventual enlightenment was supposed to come with the experience of the 'atman' (or individual soul) being at one with the 'Brahman' (the universal soul) and when I would see myself as God! Neither did I know that the same Holy Spirit who raised Jesus from the dead, and who indwells Christians today, would come and dwell in me if I asked the resurrected Jesus into my life.

One Christian writer* postulated Satan's system of logic in this way: 'God could not create something from nothing; therefore everything must be part of God; since God cannot be divided into parts, then everything is God and God is everything.' By the end of my 'search' into alternative medicine I was blinded by this sort of logic and I was a Hindu. I didn't call myself a Hindu; few Hindus do. Hinduism is a religion quite special to the Antichrist. Apart from occult healing, the other things I was into also focused on Hinduism; all the Lord has shown me since reveals more about Hinduism. It is promoted everywhere, but it's not called Hinduism!

As a searcher, I prayed to an Indian god. He is alive today, a human being with an earthly body. As a serious searcher I found the god who is said, even by Christian

---

* *Peace Prosperity and the Coming Holocaust* by Dave Hunt – Harvest House, USA (1983).

writers, to be perhaps the most powerful psychic in the world today. My experience of this man was both on film at a private viewing in a London basement, and at a shrine on the outskirts of London. Also his presence was manifested to me on a London railway station. Without hesitation I can say he is a man capable of tremendous miracles, but he is deceived, and I was deceived. The miracles were counterfeit. However, they were still miracles. They are done in the power of Satan by a man walking in the flesh, as the antichrist in the flesh will one day do them. They are not some sort of conjuring trick as I have heard some mature Christians suggest. Christians need to grasp – contradictory though it may sound – the power and reality of counterfeit miracles. They also have to grasp the nature of the spiritual power, and the significance of the results that are achieved, in occult alternative medicine.

A ten pound note can be counterfeited. It can, through the quality of the deception, present a real challenge to the Bank of England. It can perhaps circulate for years before it is discovered. So it can be with Satan's deceptions! The note is not an illusion nor a theatrical conjuring trick; it circulates just like a real note. Some of these notes might even be the same as the real notes. All they lack is the authority of the bank.

Counterfeit healing miracles really do happen. I was miraculously cleared of a complaint that had troubled me daily for eighteen years. The power of Satan to remove symptoms is not an illusion. It is a biblical truth. Matthew 24:24 speaks of false Christs and false prophets, in the *plural*: '*For false Christs and false prophets will appear and perform great miracles to deceive even the elect – if that were possible. See I have told you ahead of time.*' According to the sense of the Greek, the elect *can* indeed be deceived. Surely we can see that happening in these days, but with the truth in our hearts we can take our minds off the question, 'Does it work?' and be open to receive discernment as to the source.

110

According to the prevailing thought in western society, the surest way to unpopularity is to appear critical of the ways of others. 'Live and let live!' is a popular phrase. The churchman might misrepresent Matthew 7:1 *'Do not judge, or you too will be judged'*. Many a hippie 'did his own thing', took the drug trail to Northern India and Nepal, and ended up in hell. The Bible way is that we should look out for one another. The Hindu doctrine, having no problem with apparent contradictions, is that each person has to discover his own code of conduct. This doctrine of 'dharma' is with us in the west; it might aptly be called 'live and let die'.

The Hindu way of accepting all other religions invites an inevitable difficulty for the Bible-believing Christian. He loves the Hindu but, unlike the rest, he cannot accommodate his religion. Christians believe in the reality of an eternal life in heaven or in hell. The Hindu belief is in reincarnation and in the impersonal force that is in everything. The Hindus in the east, and their unknowing disciples in the west, still need to hear from Bible-believers of the reality of the Creator and living God.

The truth is in the Bible where it says, *'all scripture is God-breathed'* (2 Tim 3:16). Both Hinduism and occult medicine are detestable to the Lord (Deuteronomy 18:10–12). After the serpent's lie came the fall of man. Whatever the serpent said, Eve *was* going to die spiritually. What the serpent said made sense according to Eve's thinking, and the serpent's lies are believed by the world today.

Alternative medicine, and this all-embracing religion of Hinduism which pervades so much of it, are the weapons Satan is using today to bring spiritual death. See how the logic ran in the Garden of Eden. You shall not surely die. You will be like God. By persuading Eve to eat of the tree of knowledge, Satan implied that this knowledge (the 'enlightenment' or 'cosmic consciousness' of the occultists) was the key to godhood. Satan tries to persuade us that the universe, and all in it, is a self-existent unity rather than God's creation: 'How could any tree cause death if it grows out of the same ground as other trees that sustained life? All is one by virtue of the Force that is all and is in all.'

Increasingly the world is coming to the Hindu view that God is not separate from his creation. The lie of Eden that we shall not die is perpetuated by the Hindu belief in reincarnation. I believed in reincarnation until the day I asked Jesus Christ into my life. For me, as for so many others, this belief, rather than a belief in heaven and hell, was the inevitable result of my progress in occult alternative medicine. The lie of Eden, that we shall be like God, reflects the Hindu view that all is one, with its echo that we are all God.

Those who attempt healing in the spiritual realm are inviting demons to manifest counterfeits, unless they know Jesus and have the right to use His name. The implication that the tree of knowledge brings godhood seems justified when it is discovered that life's mysteries can be discovered by moving into a dimension once unknown. After discovering the counterfeit peace that comes from yoga, the modern-day housewife moves on. Eventually she may well experience 'astral projection' and feel herself leaving her body. For the Hindus, and those who do move on, there is the feeling of unity with all around them and with creation. They can become aware of energy flows through them and from them. They recognise a power which may lead them to lay hands on the sick, to contact the dead, to work magic, and so on. It's a complex deception from beginning to end. The dead are *not* contacted.

Spiritualists cite the Scripture (1 Samuel 28) where the witch of Endor brought up Samuel from the dead at the request of Saul. There are different interpretations of this text. Even Bible language can be difficult, but the Holy Spirit is available to quicken to us the truth of God's word. When, God, through His word, speaks terror into the lives of sinners, He will open a door of hope if they repent. However those that go running to the gates of hell for help in the manner of King Saul must expect to find darkness there without any shafts of light. If it is the case that God permitted the devil to deceive Saul, 'as one who refused to love the truth' (2 Thess 2:10–11), there is no way for spiritualists to get any comfort from it. Samuel and Saul lived under the old covenant, but whatever power Satan may have had under the old covenant was taken back by Jesus when he went down into hell for us and triumphed over Satan (Colossians 2:15). Also, in I Samuel 28:15 we read, 'Samuel said to Saul, "Why have you disturbed me by bringing me up?"'. We can take it that it was Samuel and not a demon speaking, and so it is clear on any interpretation that the dead are never contacted.

Language fails! But with the Bible we can have revelation; another lesson is clear from the witch's occult sin. The Bible doesn't describe the detail of *how* the witch 'brought up Samuel.' This is consistent with God's position in other Scriptures: '*Everyone has heard about your obedience so I am full of joy over you; but I want you to be wise about what is good and innocent about what is evil*'. (Romans 16:19); '*Now I say to you . . . who do not hold to her teaching and have not learned Satan's so-called deep secrets (I will not impose any other burden on you) only hang on to what you have until I come.*' (Revelation 2:24). The Scriptures are clear and they forbid our coveting to know 'Satan's so-called deep secrets.' Many Christians today, fired by the question 'Does it work?', are wanting to look deeper and deeper into what is occult alternative medicine. The Lord says to us today that He wants us to be 'innocent about what is evil.' We can receive God's discernment so that we may know what is of Him.

Of course Hindus, New Agers and occultists *do* work magic. The Bible says this is possible. However the occult medical magicians described in this book do not *heal* the sick. Satan gave Eve, and he gave Saul, a delusion. What we see in occult alternative medicine is a delusion of healing. Demons may take away the symptoms, but there is a worse physical, emotional or spiritual price to pay.

The pattern doesn't seem to vary much, and perhaps there is no reason to suppose Satan has any different outline plan for all the people. All who are being directed by Satan are on their way, whether they understand it or not, to that 'enlightenment' experience, which has many descriptions, and to eventual spiritual and eternal death. Meanwhile man, who is in Satan's grip in the area of the occult, will perhaps come to the position where a whole new world enfolds. If he is a scientist, he will see how the physical laws on which he had depended do not always apply; he will write 'new' science based upon his experience. If he has a mind to the health professions, he might become a powerful 'healer'. Through the steadfast working out of his original plan in the Garden of Eden, Satan is seeing many in the west become powerful psychics.

A knowledge of Scripture is needed. God spoke through Hosea and said, '*my people are destroyed from lack of knowledge*' (Hosea 4:6). Paul told the Romans that the Israelites were zealous for God, '*but their zeal is not based on knowledge*' (Romans 10:2).

It is not so long ago that the only obvious expressions of Hinduism were confined to the drug-based spirituality of the hippie movement and to extraordinary trend setters like the Beatles with their venture into Transcendental Meditation. Satan takes Hindu evangelism very seriously! Who ever heard of a Hindu evangelist! They are in fact everywhere without knowing it; they have been dear to Satan's heart from the beginning! It has been described as a rich jungle that has grown and spread in tropical profusion.

Today we can see clearly how this oldest of religions is invading science and the arts. It is invading medicine and the church. In Chapter Sixteen a view is taken of

114

the apostate church in Britain today. I believe there will be a coming together of the church and alternative medicine and with this I believe we shall see a reinforcement of the Hinduism to which both are open.

PART THREE
HEALING, THE CHURCH AND THE NEW AGE MOVEMENT

12: The New Age movement

Satan's bride

Since writing the First Edition of this book I have travelled in America with my eyes open! In Britain too, I believe the Holy Spirit is quickening us to what is still little known among Bible-believing Christians – the New Age movement.

It is not a bureaucracy or an organisation but a network of social and spiritual movements. Each is self-sufficient. Not one of them is essential to the whole, but the New Age movement is becoming an evident source of potential power. The network is much greater than the sum of its parts.

Behind the New Age movement is Lucifer's desire to be worshipped as God. I believe that, as Jesus Christ prepares His bride (His church), Satan prepares his counterfeit in the New Age movement. New Agers comprise many who have had their minds emptied by such practices as yoga, and who have come, or are coming, into a spiritual awareness in Satan's realm rather than in God's. They comprise also those who support social organisations, more worldly than spiritual, but which often evidence a marked denial of the teachings of Jesus. Often the organisations have an eminently respectable front. Then there are the seemingly endless movements concentrating on self and humanistic psychology. Many, if not all, are focusing on the creation.

Of course we should respect the creation, and some

organisations which are intent on protecting it are in the New Age network which at this stage comprises both the spiritual and the worldly. They are bound together by their focus on the creation, whether set to discover the 'so-called deep secrets' referred to in Revelation 2:24, or to preach about 'peace', mankind and looking after the creation.

New Agers will reach the end planned for them by many alternative routes – unless they turn to Jesus. They progressively find greater unity with one another, reaching their enlightenment in various ways hardly noticed by the world. The world knows the routes that are less obviously spiritual, like alcohol and rock music. Modern variations which Satan seeks to use to lead us to the same place have already been touched on in this book.

The rainbow

Individuals may realise they are part of a movement, or they may not. Even so, they attend at the same festivals, read similar magazines and meet in the same vegetarian or health food establishments. More and more, both the New Agers 'exploring' the mysteries of the creation, and those wanting to 'protect' the creation, are found displaying the sign of the rainbow. They are familiar with the sign of the rainbow, and in the New Age it has its counterfeit meaning. It seems that in the New Age we have a movement that meets the scriptural description of the needs of the Antichrist and of the political movement that will bring him to power.

The rainbow is used to signal others in the network. They place them in their shops and motor-car windscreens. Christians seeing the symbol used in this way may well get witness in their spirit to discontinue using the sign themselves; it would be natural for the forces of darkness to encourage use among Christians, and what use is a symbol like this to those who are in the

Kingdom? 'Who but a fanatic would bother about a rainbow symbol? After all, it's God's symbol!' Some may say that, but God's symbol to us is the *real* rainbow we see in the sky after the rain.

The New Age rainbow is a hypnotic device and New Agers call it an 'International Sign of Peace.' For them it signifies their building of a rainbow bridge between man and Lucifer, according to the spiritual tradition of the American Indians.

A newly-published children's story attracted my attention and excitement when, as a searcher, I was attending the World Assembly of Moral Rearmament in 1981. The story ends with an Indian grandfather telling his young grandson that the rainbow is a sign from 'Him who is in all things' that mankind is one big family. The youngster is encouraged to go to the top of the mountain, grow in the skills of manhood and learn to be a warrior of the rainbow, and to be one whose strong and obedient spirit will, through love, rise above the fear and hate in the world in order that destruction and war will be at an end.

The sign of the union of all people like one big family is a subtle deception and a twisting of God's truth. Whatever opposes God's truth is a lie. The lie is being promoted in different ways; today's New Agers are carrying on Satan's tradition. They are building a Rainbow Bridge, 'the antakarana', in the same way the Indians did, between Satan and mankind.

The stage is being set now

Networking groups are open to the idea of the same interconnecting 'force' or 'energy' given to eastern religions. Christians know that one day we shall see the Antichrist, and we await the return of Jesus. Many of the new 'religious' New Agers we are seeing in the west, like the Hare Krishna people we see in our High Streets, are often expecting the return of someone too. The Jews

119

still await their Messiah. The Buddhists await the Fifth Budda. The Moslems await the Imam Mahdi. The Hindus await Krishna. No doubt the same Antichrist will satisfy them all.

On all fronts, pieces of the world jigsaw are fitting together and making a bigger and bigger network. The money system is near to collapse. A card payments system is ready to be brought in. There is increased use of '666', another of the symbols used by New Agers.

The stage for the Antichrist is being set now. Surely it is not in the nature of Satan's plan – and there is evidence in God's word – that the Antichrist will start his reign in the flesh as a sort of over-worked Secretary-General busily organising his troops and launching new symbols and brand names! The organisation has been built up over thousands of years! The scenario is there for those who have ears to hear (Revelation 13:9) and eyes to see. When the Antichrist is eventually known, doubtless the world will be ready to receive him. Will more and more see that this is in fulfillment of Bible prophesy, or will many be blinded to God's word? The world is happy to be served by 'great signs and miracles' performed by the false Christs in these days. How much more will the world be ready to receive and respect the miracles of the Antichrist when he is among us? Will the rainbow be ever more widely used across the world and be ready for the Antichrist to use as his own? Will it be seen that Satan could hardly have found a better symbol than the sign God gave to Noah, for his counterfeit in the New Age? Will Christians get more and more revelation of the end-time message from Scripture? Will Satan's counterfeits for the New Age become more and more credible, even as they become more obviously incredible to those who have eyes to see? Do Christians perceive that the revolution in occult medicine fits into Satan's greater design? Do we know, and have it clearly written in our hearts, that what is foretold in Scripture cannot fail to come to pass?

The New Age can only be recognised as such when compared to the reality found through the knowledge of the person of Jesus. The world has been ready for a lead. Biblical Christianity has always provided the answer. However, through the failure of our churches, it has been the New Age movement that seems to have come up with the solution. New Age leaders, unlike so many church leaders, have spoken clearly. It is the New Agers who have demonstrated the ways to change, whether from an immoral life-style to a more moral one, from denatured bread to the organic loaf, from consumerism to economic simplicity, from drugged childbirth to natural childbirth, from the excesses of modern medicine to individual healing 'of the whole person', and so on. These changes are good. The counterfeiter always starts with something good. On the evidence of what many are seeing to be clearly good, a wide cross section, from vegetarians to veterinarians, are being drawn into holistic health.

Blinded by science

We have been blinded by science for only a few generations. The wealth of the learning and research is stacking up all around us. It continues to be true that ninety per cent or more of all the scientists that ever lived are still alive today. Science goes further and further into specialisation. If a scientist has shown something to work, it has come to be called 'truth'. This applies to all science; of course medical science is no exception. However, in these days, many scientists working in specialised disciplines are crossing over, not only into areas they don't understand, but also over the threshold into the areas of 'Satan's deep secrets' we read about in Revelation 2:24.

My own study of biofeedback and alpha waves was laid before me by scientists. The so-called scientific inventions of Kirlian photography and radionics, and the

121

so-called discovery of biorhythms, and all the rest of the variations on the same occult deception, has taken scientists back into areas of knowledge practised by eastern mystics going back thousands of years. Throughout occult medicine and the rest of Satan's realm, modern man is putting scientific descriptions to the hidden knowledge that has been available since the fall of man to those who will turn from the truth.

I do not know where the line is drawn and where science ceases to be science. It is clear however that many scientists are deceived, and many of their 'discoveries' are deceptions from across the forbidden threshold. God will provide the discernment we each need in our own situations when we earnestly seek it. Similarly Satan will deceive us when we remain open to him.

'If it works, it is OK' is still the silent message that comes forth from the medical profession. Psychiatry too, is supposed to have a basis in science. I have heard of at least one psychiatrist converted to an eastern religion as a consequence of counselling a patient. Deception is stacked upon deception. How far this penetrates the scientific discoveries of the years' past may one day be revealed to us.

Computer networking

Computers appear to be scientific. Clearly they will be significant as we move through the New Age. If there is no deception in them, then man can at least use them to deceive. The computer network will transfer and pass on deceptive information, broadcasting it at a speed not limited by time.

'Networking' is a New Age word. It is used wherever New Agers are to be found, and in July 1984 I visited the 'Networks 84' Computer Exhibition at the Wembley Conference Centre in London. Although I am a chartered accountant, there was little I could easily understand. As I moved from stand to stand I was at a loss to know how to start any sort of dialogue. The jargon was endless, making conversation very difficult. I found occult symbols, such as pyramids, placed ornamentally in a manner of a vase or table lamp.

I attended the 'Mind-Body-Spirit Festival 84' at Olympia, London on the same day as the 'Networks 84' Exhibition. Here I learned more about Networking – the 'Peace Network' and 'Networking the Networks'. The Peace Network, according to the leaflet I was shown, was 'linking ideas, people and computers to build a more peaceful world.' The system of 'Networking the Networks' enabled those participating to feed information (people, places, resources, events) for the use of others, into the computer system. While the multinational corporations are having their needs met by computers, and whilst they are probably still in the forefront of computer applications, it is clear that costs have been so reduced, and applications made so flexible, that the information and communication, once the preserve of the wealthy, are now available to the ordinary folk who have a mind to change the world. Computers provide us with enormous benefits, but they will be enormously significant in the New Age. *'He who has an ear, let him hear.'* (Revelation 13:9).

Beyond the social gospel

The world moves from one counterfeit to another, from the excesses of scientific medicine to holistic health care, from the consumer society and dead religion to the New Age and the powerful religion that lurks around the corner. Anyone who belongs to a church that offers only a short-changed spirituality will have no biblical standard against which to measure the wiles of Satan. Often it is a church itself, dynamic and alive, that leads its people, beyond the 'social gospel' so well known in the traditional church, taking them even further from a walk with the living God.

Typical groupings in the new age

As various ecology groups have sprung up in the New Age, it was inevitable that Christians would become involved. What we see is a focus on a oneness with each other and creation, on 'peace' and on what we find in nature. One group professes Christ, but New Age elements can be identified. Vegetarianism, the status of animals and the feminine role are subjects significant to them as they focus on what they see as God's 'Green World'. The world has no difficulty with that. Satan, the ruler of this world, will happily encourage it. As Christians we cannot take our eyes off Jesus; Satan is ready for the undiscerning. When we become dissatisfied with what we have, it is tempting to look around. There is no lack of provision as any 'searcher' will know well!

'The Christian Community' has centres across the world. It came about when another group of caring people felt the growing irrelevance of orthodox church life in meeting the disastrous events in world history and in understanding what they describe as the 'increasing complexities of man's inner experience.' Their search led them to Rudolf Steiner, the founder of Anthroposophical Medicine already referred to in Chapter Five. Through Steiner, we are told, a new approach to 'sacramental life' was given and 'The Christian Community will naturally turn to his work for inspiration and guidance.'*

Other communities have been established, some more avowedly Christian than others, committed variously to working for peace and justice, establishing radical life-styles and to holistic medicine. Jesus died to give us a peace that passes all understanding; that is not the peace

* *What is the Christian Community?* by Michael Tapp (Floris Books).

that the world seeks. Although the majority of these people are believed to be professing Christians, their movements have largely kept their commitment free of explicit reference to prayer and the Bible in order to make it possible for any person of goodwill to join in what they see as a matter of concern for the whole human family. Well-intentioned movements like these have stumbled into the New Age, often without realising it. Whilst they wouldn't want to be associated with occultism, Eastern religions or even Moral Rearmament, they occupy a significant place in the developing world view with eyes off the Creator but on the creation.

There is so much that could be valuable in these movements, but as things stand this is like the bait in a trap. Those who are feeling defeated or, like the founders and leaders of these movements, want to do something about the darkness that is upon the world, are looking for more than they see the world is able to give. However they can do nothing apart from knowing Jesus and turning to Him as their Saviour and Lord. It is the method of the ruler of this world to set the hearts of men on *anything* that will take their eyes off *Him*. Under the New Covenant, having received Jesus into our lives, we are New Creations in Christ Jesus and our bodies are the temples of the Holy Spirit. He wants to live our lives for us if we will let Him. He wants us to live by the power of the Holy Spirit. He wants to prove His sufficiency in every area of our lives. He wants us to join in the life of the community, but our ways are not His ways, and His ways are not man's ways.

The willing heart of the New Ager

When I was a New Ager I didn't give much thought to the particular churches I knew at that time. However, had I been comparing myself to many in the New Age and in these churches, the comparison would have been to two different extremes. The absence of life in the churches was to be contrasted with the New Age people who in one way or another were willing to spend hours each day in various efforts or arduous self-discipline. I was finding people who were starting life again, from scratch, building new life-styles away from consumerism and materialism, and who were, like the committed Christians I now know, prepared to bear without any hostility any derision that they received. They were deceived in spite of their efforts. However, had they turned to the churches that most of them knew, they would have found there no valid alternative.

The only answer is Jesus. Most New Agers, so often wanting to give so much, and so full of care for their fellow men, have never been in a place where they have heard the gospel of Jesus. Many had been regular churchgoers. Yet they never knew what Jesus himself said: *'I tell you the truth, unless a man is born again, he cannot see the Kingdom of God.'* (John 3:3) They don't know that a new life-style is not the same thing. They don't know they are on a Hindu path, and that as they progress, they will be ever more blinded to the idea of being born again.

13: From New-Ager to End-Timer

I didn't think of myself as a New Ager! Yet that is what I was. Apart from my involvement with alternative medicine, I belonged to many of the organisations that make up the New Age movement, that network of groups looked at briefly in the previous chapter that is unknowingly making the way ready for the one world ruler and the false prophet – the beast out of the sea and the beast out of the earth written about by John in the book of Revelation.

New Age and occult background

At the age of forty-three, my spiritual awakening began with a new awareness of Moral Rearmament, and from there Satan took me into occult healing. In recent years I had been active in politics too, and at the time of my 'search' my political interests also took a significant turn. Before eventually resigning all the offices I held, I joined other organisations concerned with peace and justice. It was some time after my conversion that I could discern these as being really New Age organisations. It was much later still when I took a new view of my membership of these other organisations.

Now, outside of the political 'main line' where I had spent three years as a constituency party chairman, I was seeing a unity among groups. They were facing up to the nuclear and other threats to the creation and to personal freedom. That had become my New Age focus. I had not yet joined the body of Bible-believing Christians who were in Christ's Kingdom and who were becoming increasingly aware that we must be in the end of the end times. As a non-religious individual, I was now identifying with some who were religious, but their expectation was of a false messiah of one sort or another. I hadn't yet learned that Jesus would be back soon.

Focusing on both wings of the New Age movement – the **occult exploration** of Satan's mysteries in the creation and the **protection** of that creation – I was missing the Creator. I didn't know that man had been created in order to have fellowship with the Creator. I didn't know that was what the Bible said. Mine was a New Age that *man* would build.

Unlike many New Agers, who unashamedly acknowledge the headship of Satan, I didn't think in terms of Satan either. I had learned 'healing' from a man who has been described as probably the most gifted psychic in the western world. I had prayed to an Indian 'god' and knew of his healing miracles. Many regard him as the most powerful psychic in the whole world. I had been 'healed' myself by a spiritual healer. However, by God's grace I was saved. My free will could never be taken from me. I asked Jesus into my life and by the miracle of being born again I came into the new life found in Jesus.

Whilst many New Agers are awaiting a one world leader according to their faith or tradition, as a Bible-believing Christian I was soon to see what God says in His word. The part of my testimony that follows doesn't relate directly to healing or alternative medicine. However it is included to put into a wider context what *Christians* are discerning in alternative medicine. *The world* will see the growth in alternative healing methods more and more in the context of the New Age. *Christians* will begin to see it more and more in the context of Bible prophecy.

For false Christs and false prophets will appear and

perform great signs and miracles to deceive even the elect – if that were possible. (Matthew 24: 24)
No-one knows about that day or hour, not even the angels in heaven, nor the Son, but only the Father. As it was in the days of Noah, so it will be at the coming of the Son of Man. For in the days before the flood, people were eating and drinking, marrying and giving in marriage, up to the day Noah entered the ark; and they knew nothing about what would happen until the flood came and took them all away. That is how it will be at the coming of the Son of Man. . . . Therefore keep watch, because you do not know on which day your Lord will come. . . . So you must be ready, because the Son of Man will come at an hour when you do not expect him. (Matthew 24: 36–44)

We do not know the day or the hour. We do not really know if it is to be pre-tribulation or post-tribulation when Jesus will return. We *do* know the bridegroom is preparing the bride.

Neither do we know the day or the hour of the world ruler and false prophet of Revelation 13. Yet surely Satan is already preparing the world to receive him. Christians and non-Christians alike are being deceived by Satan's wiles, perhaps as never before, as the bride is made ready.

I was always a peaceful sort of person. The New Agers are peaceful people. They identify with the occult, which is powerful, and not with materialism and politics. They have a remarkable unity, powerfully supported by the god of this world. The Bible says the earth's inhabitants will be called upon to worship the one world ruler (Revelation 13: 12) and the New Age bride is being made ready.

What further evidence is there that the time of the one world ruler may not be far off? The evidence for the end of the end times can be seen in many Scriptures. However, I continue my own testimony and, I trust, throw further light on developments in the New Age. Satan is busy in everything that is 'New Age.' I have found that some Christians, having no testimony of Satan's supernatural working in their own lives that they have recognised, have difficulty in discerning the New Age scene and indeed in seeing Satan at work in alternative medicine. I trust this testimony which God gave me will be of some help to them.

Commerce, finance, 666 and the end-times

Up to the time of searching in the occult realm, I was a businessman. I studied economics and government at university, and most of my working life had been spent in senior positions in commerce and finance, mainly with large international corporations.

Until I knew Jesus Christ I didn't have any *clear* understanding of inflation and the money system. I didn't understand the nature of inflation. I didn't know the dollar was weak. I didn't know that borrowing and overspending had galloped to such an extent that the dollar was bound to collapse. The Lord took me to this understanding by way of His word in Revelation 13: 16–18. '*He forced everyone, small and great, rich and poor, free and slave, to receive a mark on his right hand or on his forehead, so that no-one could buy or sell unless he had the mark which is the name of the beast or the number of his name. This calls for wisdom. If anyone has insight, let him calculate the number of the beast, for it is man's number. His number is 666.*'

The Bible spoke to me in Revelation 13 about the world ruler and the false prophet who forced everyone to receive a mark on his right hand or on his forehead. Without this they were unable to buy or sell. We are told that with insight and wisdom we can calculate the number of this beast, and the Bible actually gives the number; it is 666. Then I read in Revelation 14 of the description of the eternal destination for those that take the mark and worship the world ruler (the beast).

I studied the coding system* we see on our groceries. I could see that 666 always appears in the bar coding. I could understand how the debit card would come in and replace the credit card, and I could see that 666 was in evidence on some cards as well. The computers were now so advanced that all banking could be with a card, without cheques or cash. I found this was already happening in various trial locations. It seemed logical, at least, that when the world's money system did collapse, as it would through the collapse of the dollar, this would be a time to bring in the 'cashless society' or card system. The security risks of the card system are formidable and have already been reckoned; there already exists the technology and equipment invisibly to tattoo the card detail on the forehead and the right hand. As I write this, there has just come to hand the details of a Christian Newsletter from California. I read that 6,000 in Sweden in a practical experiment, involving real buying and selling, have taken a mark. The mark is registered in a computer. It is a mark for life, it was painless, it was put on by a 'ray gun', and it will register in banks or wherever those marked decide to shop. The shopkeeper, we are told, simply runs an electronic pen over the mark and it instantly sends the customer's number to a computer centre from where all information of their transactions is sent to their bank. No money needs to be touched.

Subsequently it was confirmed that the mark was on the right hand, and the location for the experiment was the south-eastern part of Sweden. It was learned in Sweden that similar experiments were being carried out in Japan and in one Latin American country. Also in Sweden, one senior bank official made a remark that

* see *The New Money System* by Mary Stewart Relfe, PO Box 4038, Montgomery, Alabama 36104, U.S.A. (1983)

seems significant. He thought the public weren't quite ready for the system yet but that the government might make it mandatory in two years.

We live in a world that has now gone far along the road of deception. Satan has blinded and made ears deaf. *'He who has an ear let him hear. If anyone is to go into captivity, into captivity he will go. If anyone is to be killed with the sword, with the sword he will be killed. This calls for patient endurance and faithfulness on the part of the saints.'* (Revelation 13: 9–10) My prayer is that Christians make ready for the bridegroom and at the same time be alert to the enemy's devices in the New Age. Christians can see that the world is deceived. When we meditate on God's word, we can see that prophecy is being fulfilled. God is always faithful to His word, and what is written *must* come to pass.

14: 'Healing' and cancer 'help' centres

The New Age is seeing the *organisation* of alternative medicine. We see the growing interest in the apostate churches. We see its infiltration into churches that Satan is bringing into that state. We see the opening of more 'Healing Centres' of every kind. As with the 'alternative medicines' themselves, the variety of establishment is seemingly endless. They can be headed up by people who would (quite fairly) describe themselves as 'leading psychics' with 'specialist' establishments. Others, more subtly, can be offering therapies which, away from the occult would be valuable. Often today they are supersmart and sophisticated. Whatever its image there may well be a variety of therapies on offer. It could be mainly a healing centre, beauty parlour, health food store or whatever. Therapies on offer alongside the 'cosmetic camouflage', the 'beauty therapy' and the 'simple food bar' will in these days include acupuncture, reflexology, relaxation, yoga and all the rest! The centres vary and yet they are the same! Small town establishments are springing up. Large retail chains now specialise in health foods with homoeopathic remedies, self-hypnotism cassette tapes, books on 'healing' and so on.

Satan will invariably latch on to what is good; he often starts with a Bible truth. He may start with the leaves that are for healing according to Ezekiel 47: 12 and bring magic to bear upon them. He seeks to get us off balance. 'Focus on Jesus' becomes 'I don't exist'. We are always to focus on Jesus, but also to remember that Satan is the ruler of the world according to Scripture. He can masquerade as an angel of light, and although Jesus has won the victory on the cross, we are commissioned to battle in His name against the principalities and powers that are at work. There is much that is good in a Health Store. However, discerning Christians will beware the mixture that is to be found there in these days.

The occult is all from the same promoter and, however high-flown the motive, it is misguided. One cancer help centre in Britain is now known world-wide, after a very short time, and it is alarming to look at the lines of treatment available there:-

'Spiritual Healing', 'Faith Healing' or 'Magnetic Healing' is available from a 'Healer'. Self healing is a description given to another line of treatment there using breathing, relaxation, meditation of several types, biofeedback and imaging on Simonton lines. After self healing there is 'self enquiry' where the idea is to look into one's psychology aided by counsellors teaching several methods including Jungian, psycho-synthesis, hypnosis, etc. according to what seem to be individual needs. Also there are Bach remedies supposed to balance emotional deficiencies. They encourage other therapies such as acupuncture, herbalism and homoeopathy.

Another line of treatment is the metabolic regime which consists mainly of vitamins (some in large doses), minerals, enzymes, and immune stimulation and support. Diet is important and another line of treatment includes a three-month cleansing period. There is a raw vegetable, fruit and grain diet with little fat, no salt, no refined carbohydrates, no sugar, coffee or milk. After that people who need meat can go on to small amounts of fish, chicken and eggs.

The establishment of this centre is an extraordinary milestone in the progress of 'alternative medicine'. The lines of treatment outlined above represent a typical package found in this sort of establishment, and it is understood that they intend to expand the number of therapies. This range, and the support received from so many places, is a measure of the longing on everybody's part to find some right answers to the dreadful health problem of our age – cancer. Indeed the centre has responded to a spiritual need. Whilst its critics have majored on the lack of science, the problem is indeed in the dimension the centre has brought into focus. Also nothing should be taken away from the sincerity, commitment, care and willingness to help that lies behind the motives of this sort of centre. My plea is for discernment.

The purpose of this book is to caution that there are two realms in the spiritual dimension, and to encourage Christians mindful of their responsibility (1 Cor. 2:14) to seek the discernment to know if a particular therapy is of God.

I believe I have made it clear that spiritual therapies which are not of God are very dangerous. Commitment, care and sincerity on the part of the unknowing helpers, understandably eager to support their fellow men in the times of their greatest need, serves only to promote the activity of deceiving spirits.

The following is the testimony of a born again believer who visited the centre I have mentioned:

'In August of last year I had a mastectomy. A few weeks previously I had seen a programme about a cancer clinic. It interested me because people seemed caring, and were seeking to help and support people who had had cancer or were facing it long term.

'In hospital a young woman with a few weeks to live was seeking the Lord. She had been to the clinic and wondered if it could meet her need. I promised her I would go and see. It proved to be very traumatic.

'Making an early start, I was taken by a friend whose husband had died of cancer. We were met at the door by a sincere, very nice, caring person, but as I went into the clinic a feeling of oppression seemed to meet me. The first person I saw asked where the cancer was. They raised their hands above me. I asked if they prayed, and was told they did not. Feeling the power of the enemy,

I asked the Lord for the protection of the precious blood. I felt very vulnerable because I was so low physically, spiritually, emotionally and in every way.

'Each person that dealt with me was caring, the message coming through that if one had peace it was possible to beat or help the cancer. In the meditation session I again felt the need of the protection of the precious blood, a feeling that grew throughout the day.

'Diet was discussed. A lot of what they said was sincere, caring, and supportive of the patients. The friends and relations had sessions too. The friend that took me had the same feeling about the place.

'I had not realised before going that it was spirit healing, not Christian healing from the Lord. The spiritist healing was not really evident until one got there and read the literature that was left around for folk to read. I came back feeling it would be so important to have a Christian based clinic.'

Sally, who wrote that testimony, is, on any view, a mature born again believer with a lifetime of mission behind her. So often the error is not obvious until we look closer; Sally **visited** the centre. I have been to it too, and have been well received there. My prayer, along with a group of other Christians, has been that the place will become Christ-centred, and, failing that, that it will be closed. However the centre expands, and more centres are opening, and are well supported by influential people. The range of therapies is large. Many more therapists are being trained in these days, and it is understandable that centres open to accomodate them. In the town nearest to my home, the healing centre presents an attractive image. It seems set to grow in popularity and perhaps challenge the practitioners of medical science.

The Bible foretells the signs of the end of the age. *'Watch out no-one deceives you'* When we get man's natural initiative and drive behind the promotion of these therapies and centres, the deception will be formidable.

15: Jesus is the name above all

Many are living in fear of cancer. Particularly in the United States, the statistics show a large growth in this disease. The Imperial Cancer Research Fund tells us, 'In England and Wales, one person in four is likely to develop cancer at some time in their life and one in five will die of it.' However Jesus is the name above every name, including cancer. By His stripes we are healed, and the truth is in God's word, **not** in forecasted statistics.

The method of one New Age 'searcher' group aims to eliminate the destructive elements in the existing system of treatment so that the new holistic approach is complementary to it; also it is directed towards setting right the destructive elements within the individual which are believed to have contributed to the development of the cancer. The patient is encouraged to believe that he himself can control or even destroy the cancer, through correcting what are called the forces of personality and emotion, through counselling, psychotherapy, deep relaxation, meditation and creative visualisation. This recognises that cancer is a disease of the total system and that tumours are but an indicator of these disorders. What we need to recognise is that cancer is from Satan and that some of these cancer treatments are from Satan too. We need to be aware that there are sincere and well-intentioned groups, displaying impressive medical credentials and the language of a false spirituality, who are tapping into the wrong spiritual realm, without knowledge of Jesus, and without regard for His word.

'Jesus Christ is the same, yesterday, today and forever'

(Hebrews 13: 8); *'He took up our infirmities and carried our diseases'* (Matthew 8:17). But we must *receive* Him. (John 1:12). Jesus tells us (Matthew 7:21) that not everyone who says 'Lord, Lord' will enter the Kingdom of heaven but only he who does 'the will of my Father who is heaven'. *'Many will say to me on that day, "Lord, Lord, did we not prophesy in your name, and in your name drive out demons and perform many miracles?" Then I will tell them plainly, "I never knew you. Away from me you evildoers!"'* *(Matthew 7:22–23)*. We have to receive Jesus and to *know* Him. Plainly Jesus isn't interested in the miracles of those who don't know Him and who have no authority to use His name.

Yet in these last days thousands upon thousands are receiving divine healing at the hands of those who truly do know the Lord Jesus. Many who know Jesus are also taking authority over the sicknesses that invade their own bodies, and of course they *can* do this in Jesus' name. In contrast to the spiritual approaches to cancer without Jesus, being adopted by so many well-meaning people, there follows just one example from one who *does* know the Lord Jesus. In this example we have the testimony of a present-day disciple to the removal of a growth through the power that is in the name of Jesus:

'I got up one morning. I was drying my body, and I found that I had a lump on my breast. The Devil said to me, "Now Smartie, you've got it. What are you going to do about it?" And I sure had all the symptoms of it. I had that lump there; and I had that stabbing pain. I went straight to my Father's word. I said, "You Devil, in Jesus' name, I will not accept this. The word of God tells me that Christ has redeemed me from the curse of the law. The word of God tells me that by the Lord's stripes I am healed. Now you foul unclean thing, you've no legal right in my body. I bind you and in Jesus' name, you get out of my body. Lord, I just ask that you let your healing power flow through me and heal me, and by faith I receive my healing in the name of Jesus."

'I went to the Lord's table and I had that cup which represented the blood of Jesus, and I had that bread which represented the body of Jesus which was broken for me, and I took it in faith. But still the lump was there. Still the stabbing pains were there. So I had to make a decision. Did I really believe what I was preaching? Or did I go running back into Egypt? Did I go running back to the physicians of Egypt? God said, 'I am the God that healeth thee; thou shalt have no other gods before me." So I had to make a decision. Did I go running back to the physicians in Egypt, or did I really believe that God was the God that healeth me? I said, "Lord, I'm going to stand on your word. The Bible says, 'having done all, to stand,' so I'm going to stand, and I will not be affected by what my body is telling me. The Devil has put these symptoms upon my body and is trying to tell me that your word is not true. I know that he is a liar. I know that he is a thief, and I know that he is a robber. So I'm not going to be affected by what my body is telling me. This body, you will come into line with the word of God. By the Lord's stripes, body, you are healed." And I said, "Lord, as far as the matter is concerned, in my heart, I am healed." And I stood! And I stood! And I stood! And every single day, every half an hour of every day, the old Devil would come along with his thoughts in my mind, "What if this . . . ?" and "But what if . . . ?" You can imagine the thoughts that he is capable of putting into your head: fear, doubts and unbelief; and I said, "Devil, get out of my mind. I will not even entertain such thoughts. Get out in Jesus' name." When these stabbing pains came, I said, "I won't have it. Get out of my body. By the Lord's stripes, I am healed." And after standing for ten days, that lump started to shrivel up.

'The Devil knew I wasn't going to receive that which he was putting upon me, and I just stood. Now that lump is completely gone and there is absolutely no sign of it, and I know that the word of God is true. "Having done all to stand." I could have run back to Egypt. I could have gone back to the physicians of Egypt. And, well . . . I'd probably be without one part of my body today, who knows? But I stood on the word of God. For God's word is true.'

That testimony doesn't describe a system that can be copied or a method that can be thrust by one believer upon another. A movement in America known as 'Shepherding/Discipleship' appears to have taken some Christian fellowships to cultish extremes. We can read* of one approach in the area of healing, though not characteristic of all Shepherding groups, where the leader actually forbids the members to seek medical assistance. That is in a fellowship of born again Bible believers. The first comment of one member, who eventually sought to bring a lawsuit against the fellowship, had been, 'Who, me, in a cult? That could never happen to me!'

Despite their extremism in some areas, these fellowships are basically Christian groups who have received wrong teaching. Under the New Covenant we can all have a personal on-going relationship with Jesus. Our faith must come from that relationship and not from anywhere else. It cannot come from any new 'Group' ideas. The believer in the testimony reproduced above *has* that relationship with Jesus. Her healing came from her faith in God to honour His word when, with the authority of the name of Jesus, the offensive was taken up against Satan and his diseases.

Jesus had already been raised from the dead when He spoke to His disciples and told them to go into all the world and preach the good news and heal the sick. Jesus speaks to all of His disciples today through those words: '*And these signs will accompany those who believe: In my name they will drive out demons. . . . they will place their*

* 'Shepherding/Discipleship – Theology and Practice of Absolute Obedience' article in *Awareness* Magazine July 1984, C.I.O., 92, The Street, Faversham, Kent.

hands on sick people and they will get well.' (Mark 16:17–18) Jesus is the name above every evil spirit. Jesus is the name above cancer. Jesus is the Healer today. When we lay hands on the sick, knowing Him and believing God to honour His word, He is right there with us. He is the greatest physician.

16: Churches off the track

As well as looking critically at the 'alternative medicines' and so-called healing establishments, Christians do well from the healing point-of-view to look closely at the denominational churches. Look also at the agencies they proliferate as they move into the spiritual dimension, often with no clear view of the two realms that are to be found there.

Consider for example the Churches' Fellowship for Psychical and Spiritual Studies. The name describes the purpose of the fellowship. Do they forget that dabbling, even for the seeker after a new psychical and biblical approach to psychical or spiritual phenomena is forbidden by God and invokes Satan's spell? In a Quarterly Review in 1982 we could read that 'mediumship is a potential gift of the Holy Spirit'.

A national Anglican journal on healing recently featured the healing practised by the Healer whose radio programme started me off on the 'search'. Before that search eventually led me to Jesus I had attended his training centre and he had been one of my teachers.

Scripture allows no grey area between God and Satan. My own passage from darkness into light was a remarkable miracle. I had met with many caring and sincere teachers and I had witnessed their power to 'heal'. I do not know how to explain what it means to be a new creation to those who are working counterfeit miracles. I do not know how to explain it to many in the churches.

It is clear we have many apostate churches which have departed so far from the truth that unity with them is impossible.

Recently I attended evensong at a major Anglican church. The proposed extension of its healing ministry was described on the notice board outside, but to enter I had to pass through a T'ai Chi class in progess in the church hallway.

Beware also books on spiritual subjects, which have only a *superficial* Christian appearance. In books brought to the discerning it can soon become clear where there is error. A foreword by a former bishop for example, provided no clue to the status of the healing sanctuary the author (himself a clergyman) had set out to describe. Another foreword by a different former bishop once again gave a credibility to what was therein discussed. The subject was acupuncture!

God is no respecter of persons; we are all equal before Him. We do well as Christians to test all ideas for error. Without discernment this is so easily mixed with truth.

At a CPC* conference recently I was shown for the first time a book for which the Holy Spirit had prepared me some months previously. It was *Healing The Family Tree* by Dr. Kenneth McAll. The publishers had described it as controversial, but such a book needed discernment more than discussion. The cover described the author's amazing gift and how he discovered a remarkable new method of healing. A book from the occult (which I had burned when I came to know Jesus) was referred to in it and a quick follow-through showed no hint of disapproval by the author. Progess through

* CPC (Caring Professions Concern) is a Christian perspective for the caring professions involving Christian doctors and other health workers. It has pastoral concern for the 'carers' and a 'prophetic' concern for the 'people'. 'Without a vision the people perish' and without a vision the caring professions will also perish. The aim is for the prophetic voice to be heard speaking the heart of God with clarity into the caring professions through Christians prepared to live up to a high calling in Christ.

the book provided confirmation upon confirmation of the initial discernment.

I believe the Lord taught me a lesson through this book. It was clear to me the book wasn't Holy Spirit led and I marked line after line that jarred with my spirit. Then one day I was asked by two mature Christians, one a general medical practitioner, to go through the book with them to explain my objections. For two hours I attempted to do that. I failed. I couldn't convey what the Holy Spirit was so clearly saying, and about halfway through the book the three of us gave up. I hadn't convinced them on a single point. 'But we can see you are right about the book,' they told me afterwards. The Lord had given them discernment too. This book is a plea for the exercise of spiritual discernment. We can only receive it from Him. Some have written to me evidencing that same discernment; on the other hand it seems a great number of Christians remain deceived. One review described it as an important book and then went on to reproduce its errors. Then I was greatly encouraged to read in a later issue of the same publication, a warning by the editor to readers about the book. He quoted an Australian authority who has recognised much of the teaching of this book to be similar to that of the Spiritualist Church, and rooted in the occult. I believe more Christians must speak out and admonish with all wisdom (Colossians 3: 16). Often it seems there are but a few who spot deceptions, and when they do, so often it seems they do not speak out.

I have related those areas that I believe God has specifically brought to my attention. Nearer to where I live, I have twice been led to visit one particular church. Each occasion was for the visit of a psychic 'healer'. Once I was a 'searcher' in Satan's kingdom, and once a member of God's Kingdom.

Beware therefore those places and those leaders who once brought glory to God but where in these days Satan appears to be dimming the light. Prayer is needed for the *real* leaders in our established church for they have many in their ranks who, far from having discernment, do not even believe that Jesus Christ is the Son of God. And yet they may have a ministry for 'healing'!

We can no longer afford to ignore the spiritual status of those that minister healing to us – that goes for the churches as well as for the whole field of medicine.

Visiting a cancer help centre in 1983, I had seen the occult with a *medical* label; I saw occult therapies gaining more respectability. In 1984, I hoped I would not see a parallel situation, with a *Christian* label, when I made a special journey to London to attend the monthly healing service at the church I mentioned earlier, a place I believe God had put on my heart since stumbling into the T'ai Chi class being held in the church the year before. On my journey I was able to read a magazine devoted to healing, and connected with this church. The magazine, still asking the wrong dangerous question, 'Does Alternative Therapy Work?' in its front page headline, set out the 'Order of Service' I would be attending that evening.

I was conscious of the need for unity. However I had read what David Watson had written* about the two main dangers for believers: 'One is unity where there ought to be division, the other is division where there ought to be unity . . . But there can be no true unity where there are basic differences over essentials of the faith, such as the deity of Christ, the atonement, justification by faith, the resurrection of Christ, the necessity of new birth or the authority of scripture.' I had fasted. I had time to pray, and I didn't know if I could be in unity with them.

A copy of an article in the London *Standard* (February 1983) on the board outside the church gave much information about the conversion of the crypt into a healing centre. There was a photograph of Princess Caroline of

Hidden Warfare by David Watson (STL Books – 1972)

Monaco and the new foundation stone commemorating her visit; work on the healing centre had begun. Also on the board was a letter from the World Health Organisation in Geneva. This serves very well to emphasise the significance of the centre on the world scene, and the interest of the World Health Organisation should not be regarded as insignificant! The letter included the following:

> It seems certain that this Centre, serving those in need of affirmation and wholeness will become a pattern for future developments in health care. As the industrialised societies become progressively more complex and bewildering, the need becomes ever more apparent, and specific action to meet it becomes an urgent demand.
> We will be watching the progress of the Centre with great interest and commend it to the generosity of those you approach.

The burden of Christians has to be that the Centre, when opened, will be Christ centred; the leadership at the centre will need to turn to scripture to find the path it has to travel.

The Churches' Council for Health and Healing (CCHH) seeks to help and encourage the churches. It produces a directory, *Your Very Good Health* which lists many health and healing organisations. The Council was set up 40 years ago by Archbishop William Temple; but it seems the scene now is a very different one. Striking advances have been made into occult medicine and we have to look at the CCHH as it is today.

They see the person as a whole – body, mind and spirit – in intimate and dynamic interaction. However they seem to miss some vital scriptures. *Your Very Good Health* includes groups because of the 'quality' of their work, and it describes one organisation which has the main aim of developing 'all forms of yoga.' The aim of another is to secure the passing of laws to recognise 'natural healers.' 'Health in the New Age' is another group listed. This aims to be a **bridge** between scientists, doctors, ministers of religion and practitioners of alternative medicine on the one side, and lay men on the other. At the time of the directory listing, the same charitable trust was described as advising the 'Festival of Mind, Body and Spirit'. The trust was actively promising the idea of an international association for 'Holistic Health Care' to work officially with the World Health Organisation. Also it was setting up a 'New Age Information Service' to link via computer to organisations in Europe and the United States.

Christian fellowships led by the Holy Spirit work better than synods, councils and bureaucracies. It is the same with these New Age 'networks'. They work well. One organisation listed is the 'Positive Health Network', established to develop 'wide' contacts in the area of health. Yet another organisation stated its aim as teaching the diagnosis and correction of energy imbalances. Another trust listed – well known to those of us who have moved in the occult realm – is described as helping 'seekers' to find the discipline that suits *them* best.

Throughout the Directory, I see little evidence of what *God* wants. Rather we are presented with an assortment including a great deal that is occult. There is the implicit invitation to see what suits *us* best. Indeed there is a marked absence of scripture. In the lengthy introduction, the General Secretary of the CCHH says he has 'no doubt' that the contributions of the 'ecological field', the 'personal growth movement' and the recovery of a spiritual dimension through yoga or zen, or by a return to a religious way of seeing reality, are all vital. Away from the evils evidenced in pills and depressions, the General Secretary looks optimistically to communities being 'inventive' including food habits and 'spiritual healing'.

As I read the directory I was reminded of my weekend at a retreat. I had just heard of the discovery of my fellow searcher's naked and mutilated body. My friend was dead with wounds self inflicted through demonic influences and I had, as a consequence, started to search into the dangers of my search and my discoveries. At that retreat I was able to buy another directory of the occult. Also on the notice boards I was confronted with posters and advertising of the sort I was by this time trying to escape. I remember thinking my search into the occult, then ending, could have progressed much faster, had I visited this place at the outset. The same would be true with the wealth of information the CCHH provided.

Let us also beware of counterfeit gifts even in fellowships of committed Christians. *Occult laying-on-of-hands* exists where we least expect to find it! Satan seeks to pervert the true healing in the name of Jesus. He will encourage sincere ritual healing, spoken in the name of Jesus by those who don't know Him and where it can't be truly in Jesus' name at all.

As we have seen, in Matthew 7: 21–23 Jesus is reminding us that we have to *know* Him. We must have the Holy Spirit dwelling in us if we are to do the Father's will. We need to watch out for false prophets who find platforms in Christian fellowships. We need to beware too of those ministers who, without discernment, encourage all and sundry to lay hands on other members of a congregation. In this supernatural dimension, Satan, the deceiver, awaits his opportunity; he knows the supernatural better than the finest Christian minister who will be helpless without discernment. '*But I am afraid that just as Eve was deceived by the serpent's cunning, your minds may somehow be led astray from your sincere and pure devotion to Christ.*' (2 Cor 11: 3) The truth is found in God's word. Alternative medicine is in large part a

148

counterfeit of divine healing; false prophets on the Christian circuit can present an even more subtle challenge. Discernment is essential.

17: The healing network

Alternative medicine, including the most devastatingly dangerous psychic and spiritual healing therapies, is fast growing in acceptability. It is getting itself highly organised too. We see associations and alliances that are bringing together out-and-out spiritualists with nominal, and even born again, Christians. The Confederation of Healing Organisations (CHO) was founded in 1981 and comprises nine organisations. The National Federation of Spiritual Healers, the well known and established organisation for spiritual healers, all their spiritualist associations, and the Radionic Association, are included. The Churches' Council for Health and Healing is given 'observer' status. The CHO cooperates with the Natural Health Network. Recently this body brought together delegates from all over Britain to listen to speakers on the theme 'Natural Health and its Place in Society.'

Apart from the precedents being set by the Healing Centres and some 'Christian' churches in the same period we have seen medical doctors form the British Holistic Medical Association. We have seen the formation of the British Holistic Pharmacists Association. Still in the same short period, the new monthly *Journal of Alternative Medicine* has provided excellent PR for alternative medicine. For the layman we have seen the launch of an attractive magazine *Alternative Medicine Today* which focused on Prince Charles' views in its first issue. We have seen vast numbers of new books about alternative therapies. We have witnessed the support of nominally Christian churches for all that is taking place.

Prince Charles attended a colloquium on the subject

organised by the Royal Society of Medicine, and the 'Journal of Alternative Medicine' reported (September 1984) that under Sir James Watt, Past President of the Society, it is beginning to take a leading role in offering suggestions for integrating complimentary and allopathic medicine.

The representative of the British Holistic Medical Association opened the colloquium and (according to the Journal) the central issue between allopathic and alternative medicine was seen like this:

> It would seem that the energetic or vitalistic principles which describe the body's homeostasis in many of the alternative therapies do have a sound basis in theoretical physics and chemistry. These concepts have been largely ignored by the majority of 'scientific and academic' doctors, who instead have concentrated on material phenomena, some of which are of questionable scientific value.

That seems to be a fair summary of the position between alternative and allopathic medicine as the majority of their respective practitioners see it. Also we can look at it in this way:

1. Doctors, guided as far as possible by science and intelligent observations on a 'Does it work?' basis, have indeed concentrated on material aspects.
2. These same scientifically minded doctors have hitherto, and in spite of their own use of placebo treatments, failed to see that the alternative treatments (cloaked in the deceptive ideas about energy) *do* work. At the very least they can work when faith is put in them.

Admittedly the Royal Society of Medicine has laid down criteria for collaboration, namely a recognised training programme, recognised qualifications, a self-regulatory organisation and a willingness to submit their results to research. That will naturally exclude many of the fringe alternative therapies not seen as providing a satisfactory basis for collaboration with the medical profession. Nevertheless the criteria will encourage many of the therapies and the gates will be opened to them. Next we can expect that the practitioners of the less significant therapies will not be slow in putting their houses in acceptable administrative order to get the same recognition.

For those who meet the criteria, the Royal Society of Medicine has been at great pains to avoid the term 'alternative'. They say this suggests competition between orthodox and other therapies, and they prefer the term 'complementary'.

The effect of such dialogues involving distinguished, and even learned, participants is to lend weight to the idea that alternative medicine is scientific. Additionally there is the pressure of the increasing evidence, now coming through to the general public, that orthodox medicine is not as scientific as had been supposed. Too long the medical doctors have prescribed on the basis of 'Does it work?' without knowing some of the hidden dangers; now they are being forced to look at what seem to be some very attractive alternatives. These *do* work, and it is likely they will work even 'better' given the psychology of a medical doctor's prescription and endorsement. Doctors are being led from the fairly obvious dangers that accompany many of the existing conventional treatments, into the subtle and seemingly danger-free world of the 'natural' therapies.

This swing from drugs to the even more dangerous occult therapies is a parallel of the swing seen on the seedier side of the drug world. There we see movement on from cannabis and marijuana to various forms of yoga and meditation. The prayers of Christians are urgently needed in this whole area (Ephesians 6: 18).

As the 'network' makes its bid to extend its 'healing' into the churches, Jesus still says to the unsaved in these places: '*I stand at the door and knock*' (Revelation 3: 20). He still wants us to receive from Him the wholeness He died to give us, and to be led by the power of the Holy Spirit.

Many believers remain in apostate churches and can therefore hardly escape the apostate teaching. How long dare they hang on? What example do they set the unsaved? How do they dare to bring others into fellowship there? How long can they remain there as the spiritual forces accelerate against them? How will they receive the miracles when they witness them, and how will they know if they are from Satan? Are they really strong enough to stand, even as missionaries, in a fellowship where Jesus is not Lord? Do they believe there can be fellowship when Christ is not at the centre of it? Indeed will our Lord allow unity where He is left out? Where can we find in Scripture any basis for being pastored by an unbeliever?

The Psalmist tells us, '*Blessed is the man that does not walk in the counsel of the wicked*' (Psalm 1: 1). Paul had this to say to the believers at Corinth:

Do not be yoked together with unbelievers. For what do righteousness and wickedness have in common? Or what fellowship can light have with darkness? What harmony is there between Christ and Belial? What does a believer have in common with an unbeliever? What agreement is there between the Temple of God and idols? For we are the temple of the living God. As God has said: 'I will live with them and walk among them, and I will be their God, and they will be my people.'
Therefore come out from them and be separate, says the Lord. Touch no unclean thing, and I will receive you.
'I will be a Father to you, and you will be my sons and daughters, says the Lord Almighty.'' (2 Corinthians 6: 14–18)

Ignoring Scripture will prove dangerous for believers who remain in apostate churches. Christians will need to beware when they start to see miracles at the hands of unbelievers. Jesus doesn't mind where His healing is manifested. However Satan will be especially pleased to 'heal' in the churches when the way is made open for him! Satan's healing network seems set for advances in that direction. I believe Jesus wants to work through fellowships of believers in the New Testament style; those who continue to fellowship under the ministry of unbelievers will do so at their peril.

> *There will be terrible times in the last days. People will be lovers of themselves, lovers of money, boastful, proud, abusive, disobedient to their parents, ungrateful, unholy, without love, unforgiving, slanderous, without self-control, brutal, not lovers of the good, treacherous, rash, conceited, lovers of pleasure, rather than lovers of God – having a form of godliness but denying its power. Have nothing to do with them.* (2 Timothy 3: 1–5)

Thus Paul wrote of the **form** of godliness that we know so well today.

18: The World Health Organisation and The World Council of Churches

In July 1984 I travelled to Geneva to visit the World Health Organisation (WHO) and the Christian Medical Commission (CMC) which is part of the World Council of Churches (WCC). Living away from London I very rarely see the London *Standard*. The headline caught my eye on the news stand as I passed through the airport building: 'Charles, the would-be healer.' 'I've always wished that I could heal.' Inside I read, 'From exercise to extra-sensory perception, from coping with stress to self-discipline . . . the sincere and outspoken views of the Prince of Wales.' A special four-page pull-out centred on the interview given by the Prince to a reporter at Kensington Palace.

On my journey this time, I could read how it was that Charles 'happened' to settle his eyes on a book about Paracelsus as he pondered what he would say in his speech to the British Medical Association (already referred to on page 27). I read how he believed it was only by being 'open' that we could encourage others to be the same. I recalled how 'open' I had been on the day my search into healing methods began when I just 'happened' to switch on BBC Radio at a very unusual time of the day and there 'happened' to be just starting a programme telling us of our potential as healers. Jesus was not then Lord of my life.

The next day in Geneva, the Manager of the

155

Traditional Medicine Programme at the WHO was enthusiastically copying the words from the *Standard* we had open before us. Here was a Nigerian medical doctor, fairly recently appointed to this top job in this well respected United Nations agency. But what of the World Health Organisation itself? What of its traditional medicine programme? Traditional medicine is really another description for alternative medicine, and whatever the native names, I soon established that it was a case of 'the same mixture as before.' My host and I, there in his office, were surrounded with all the evidence of occult medicine including the life-sized acupuncture chart that dominated the wall behind him.

A book,* put together by his predecessor, 344 pages of the world's traditional medicine, seemed to confirm all the indications as to the direction the WHO is headed. In his foreword to the book, Halfdan Mahler, MD, tells us of its purpose in providing a better understanding of 'traditional, indigenous and unorthodox' systems. In what seemed a significant conclusion, he writes, 'It is hoped that this information will be of use to governments when they consider the most appropriate methods for inclusion in their health strategies.'

In these days we see governments taking a new look at their health plans and training programmes. The five-year plan for traditional medicine, upon which the WHO has recently embarked, seems set to bring about a new understanding and availability of the enormous choice that there is. There is no discernment; indeed this large book has chapter upon chapter dealing with therapies clearly recognised by Christians as occult.

It is inevitably true that the basis of the medicine in the great majority of the WHO member countries is traditional rather than what we call scientific. However it is a significant sign of the times we are in, that traditional

---

* *Traditional Medicine and Health Care Coverage* (WHO – Geneva) – 1983

medicine was only incorporated into the WHO programmes as recently as 1976. In that same year the World Council of Churches shifted its perspective also. I believe the five-year programme just started is especially significant. In the jargon of the United Nations, this new 'Global Medium-term Programme 12.3 – Traditional Medicine' appears for the first time as part of 'Objective 12'. It involves the aim of fostering national and international action to achieve specified objectives by 1989. The first objective is for those countries where traditional medicine is widely practised; they are to have 'useful' traditional practices incorporated into their general system of health care. For the second objective, the WHO wants to identify at least two centres for research in traditional medicine in each region. The United Kingdom is one of the thirty-three active member states in the European Region. The Regional Office for Europe is in Copenhagen, Denmark but it would perhaps be surprising if there was not a Centre for research established in Britain. Also part of the plan is to identify as many 'traditional medicine plants or treatments' as possible.

Again predictably, 'Does it work?' is the question being asked. 'Does it come from the spiritual dimension, and if so, which realm?': that is the question to which science and Satan has blinded us.

One chapter of *Traditional Medicine and Health Care Coverage* is contributed by one of the leaders of the Holistic Health Movement from England. He deals with Anthroposophical Medicine, Autogenic Training, Bates Technique, Breathing, Biofeedback, Colour Therapy, Flower Remedies, Gerson Treatment, Healing, Hydrotherapy, Negative Ions, Radionics, Reflexology (Zone Therapy), Shiatsu, Do-In and T'ai Chi.

Could there be a place in this traditional medicine programme at the WHO for Divine Healing? I recalled that the large and glossy alternative medicine books sometimes gave one page to this. Now that the WHO had come into the spiritual and the supernatural, it occured to me there might be an openness to the idea of looking at Divine Healing. My reply came in a letter from the WHO: 'There are very firm guidelines laid down by the Organisation for its programme of traditional medicine and these preclude the possibility of integrating certain aspects of traditional medicine based on spiritual, moral or other fundamental principles.'

Only four hundred yards or so from the place of my meeting at the WHO, the Central Committee of the World Council of Churches was in session. It is undeniable that there are Christians at work in these organisations and condemnation is neither appropriate nor intended. However the likelihood of both of them having a significant part in the one-world government prophesied in the Book of Revelation must be worth mentioning. '*He who has an ear, let him hear*' (Revelation 13:9).

The Archbishop of York had left behind the problems of his office and I was able to attend the session as he shared the platform with church leaders from across the world. Just a few days before, I had opened my newspapers to see pictures of the archbishop at the consecration of an unbelieving secular, professor of theology as Bishop of Durham, and three days later, I had seen the pictures after fire had struck causing an estimated million pounds worth of damage to York Minster. However my real purpose was a meeting with the Director of the Christian Medical Commission who took time out from his especially busy schedule. Once again I seemed to be in the right place at the right time. *Document Two,* was available for all who needed it. CMC is a sub-unit of the Programme Unit on Justice and Service, and this report, produced for the distinguished assembly, contained in a nutshell what the Director was able to give me. I learned that in its role as an 'enabler', the CMC purpose is to advise and assist churches and their congregations to combat injustice, to share and to heal, by becoming involved in various 'health promotive approaches.' One of these approaches is the study of Traditional Healing Practices and how they can be integrated with allopathic medicine.

Where then does the CMC stand on alternative (or traditional) medicine? Let the Report* I was given speak for itself:

'A large part of the world practises and relies on traditional medicines today, and we have much to learn from them. They are based on local culture, and the community plays an important part as the supportive system. There are herbal medicines which are easily available, inexpensive and often very effective alternatives to expensive imported pharmaceuticals. Then there are ancient literature-based systems of medicine, such as acupuncture and acupressure in China, Ayurveda in India, Unani and equally ancient, primal, oral-based indigenous medicine practised in Africa, among the Aborigines of Australia, the Maoris of New Zealand, the Indians of North and South America and the Pacific Islanders.
Over the last decade, the CMC has urged and promoted not only a deeper understanding of traditional healing methods, but also a more effective partnership of traditional and allopathic systems of medicine. Traditional medicine has already been recognized and legalized in several countries. Several associations of practitioners of indigenous medicine have been formed around the world; traditional birth attendants (TBAs) are recognized, and training courses building on their skills and

* *Report of Programme Unit (II) on Justice & Service* World Council of Churches, Central Committee, Geneva, Switzerland. 9–18 July 1984

utilization are organized both by church agencies and the government.
The study of traditional healing practices and the contribution of traditional healers should continue. Greater attention is also to be given to the spiritual healing and the healing responsibility of the congregation.'

The year 1976 brought in a new era for the WHO. In the same year this neighbour at the WCC also shifted its attention. It moved away from an international perspective to what it calls 'a dynamic search' for the views and understanding of health workers and churches as they confront the situation in their own countries. From 1976 the CMC has sponsored workshops across the world from South East Asia in the east to the Carribean in the west. The results of these have served to bring traditional medicine into focus.

In the WCC bookshop I was offered just two books on healing and the church. One* described the localised 'search' undertaken by the CMC since 1976. Neither the title of the book nor the apparent purpose of the 'search' seemed to suggest any emphasis on traditional medicine would result, but it is not surprising the discoveries made were in *that* area.

In marked contrast was the other WCC book recommended to me; *The Healing Church*, published twenty years before, was very different in its content. However, whilst very western in its approach, my eyes caught one very small section: 'pre-scientific forms of healing'. That is a small seed that has grown. The search started, and the deception got deeper.

Pre-scientific forms of healing (alternative medicines) are filling the bookshelves today. All that is being written

* *The Search for a Christian Understanding of Health, Healing and Wholeness* (Christian Medical Commission, WCC Geneva) – 1982

is being consumed by kings and governments, church and state. They seem to have no regard to where the healing comes from.

On a positive note, the WHO has achieved a great deal through medical science and truly natural remedies. No blanket condemnation of the WHO, nor indeed of medical science, is intended in this book, and there is no suggestion that it is wrong for governments and agencies to use the hard-working and caring offices of the WHO. Indeed, its various schemes over the years have, in one area after another, eradicated malaria, yaws and other serious diseases.

PART FOUR
DRUGS AND DOCTORS

19: Why pick on 'alternative medicine'?

This is a question most commonly asked by Christian doctors when I have shared my burden for exposing occult medicine. They have spoken this question from their doubts about medical science, not about 'alternative medicine'. I accept that dependence on drugs in the National Health Service increases, notwithstanding their credibility being in decline. Such is the nature of addiction. My doctor friends are surely right when they say there is much wrong in medicine. I believe there is much that passes for medical science that must be exposed. But I write about 'alternative medicine' because it is a 'growth' business. It is an area that I know!

However, it is sensible briefly to look in on the more familiar medical scene, and I do so in this single chapter.

Drugs first: God second

During my lifetime, we have seen the enormous growth of the pharmaceutical industry and the increased readiness of doctors to prescribe what it offers. It has become normal, even for Christians, to deny the New Testament faith and life, to get the medical answer first, and ask God second. Such lack of faith can only put a brake on what the Holy Spirit can do.

The pharmaceutical industry is an international one. Research and marketing costs are understandably high. News stories of drugs like Librium and Valium are well-known; commercial considerations are to the fore in a world where Christian values are substantially ignored. Are the pharmaceutical companies perhaps the sorcerers of this age? (Deuteronomy 18:10–12).

The word 'pharmacy' comes from the Greek *pharmakeia* which means 'enchantment with drugs'. In the Book of Revelation *pharmakios* is always translated 'sorcerer'. Also, what are the origins of medicine itself? The Greek god of medicine is *Asklepios* (Latin: *Aesculapius*) and the cult of Aesculapius came to Rome in 293 B.C. when the god (a snake) was established on an island in the Tiber. Rather than the bronze snake God told Moses to set on a pole (Numbers 21:8) this seems the most likely origin of today's medical symbol which includes the serpent!

Drugs are a problem: but beware the wrong answer

In every area of life we can often spot other people's problems in amongst all the confusion; then as laymen we can often bring to them inappropriate answers. The Prince of Wales saw very clearly the problems of the medical profession in Britain during his year as President of the British Medical Association. He said: 'It is frightening how dependent we are all becoming on drugs and how easy it is for doctors to prescribe them as the universal panacea for all ills.'

More than £2,000 million is spent in Britain on drugs in a single year. By and large they only relieve symptoms. They quieten you down, or they prop you up! They bolster your confidence or they quieten your emotions.

Apart from any origins or direct merits of a drug, we have come to know about side-effects. The birth of the thalidomide babies was the foremost example. We were able to *see* the side-effects. Unlike with the thalidomide drug, doctors are in a position to make a value judgement reckoning the side-effects when prescribing steroids. The issues are perhaps difficult for some patients to assess.

164

However the list of side-effects after the long-term use of steroids is formidable and has given rise to the formation of the 'Steroid Action Aid Group'. They were represented, alongside occult practitioners, at a major exhibition – an alternative medicine exhibition – held in the 'Rainbow Suite' at one of London's major new exhibition centres.

What of the side-effects we don't see? Physical. Emotional. Spiritual. This book is essentially a look at the spiritual dimension; hypnosis opens the way for evil spirits, but what of hypnotic drugs? What actually happens when we are under anaesthetic? Medical science does not try to blind us with an answer. They do not know. The answers to all of these questions are important in spiritual terms.

Back to the alternative medicine scene, and taking a doctors' viewpoint, the BMA have set up a working party to consider 'the feasibility and possible methods of assessing the value of alternative therapies, whether used alone or to compliment other treatments.' The BMA has invited information on the techniques used in the various forms of alternative therapy and also on how these therapies are believed to work.

Drugs: the wrong kind of medicine?

In *The Wrong Kind of Medicine?** it is argued that the power of suggestion is fundamental to all systems of medicine and that medicine works partly just by concentrating the mind on cure. Whilst perhaps most drug treatments 'do not benefit patients at all', people underestimate the shortcomings of medicine and are discouraged from thinking about the possible risks and unwarranted effects that are characteristic of virtually all drugs. In this critical guide, Charles Medawar writes that

* *The Wrong Kind of Medicine* by Charles Medawar/Social Audit (Consumer Association – 1984)

commercial, professional and government interests dominate health care to an extent damaging both to the individual and to national health. The power of suggestion and hope seem to be essential factors to recovery, in the world's view, and Mr Medawar goes some way along the Christian line taken in this book, when he says it is debatable how far drugs should be used to encourage this hope.

As laymen we look for whatever evidence can be found. Two panels of experts, set up to advise an official, public enquiry into the 'Relationship of the Pharmaceutical Industry to the National Health Service' reported as long ago as 1967 that about one third of the most prescribed drug products were officially described as 'undesirable preparations.' That was in a time of soul searching following the birth of the thalidomide babies. What of the not-so-obvious side-effects, and what is the situation today?

The wrong kind of medicine is the natural response to the demands on a doctor to heal. The methods have changed since the days of Adam, but doctors were always successful. This is because whatever is taken in faith can work. Doctors are moving more into alternative therapies, and with the usual faith placed in the doctor these therapies will work especially well when *they* prescribe them.

Doctors understand the power of the placebo referred to previously, and according to the *British Medical Journal* (23 July 1970), analysis of prescriptions in the UK suggests that perhaps one third of all drugs are prescribed for this effect. Placebo is the Latin for 'I will please.' However aren't doctors almost invariably going to prescribe a drug that will have some effect rather than an inert substance coated with sugar? Otherwise, if asked, how could they explain it to the patient? It's well intentioned, but where do these deceptions end? Isn't it urgent that Christians start to put their faith for their health in Jesus?

It is here that we must part company with Charles Medawar and his most useful book. He has pointed to the most urgent need of an alternative faith; then, towards its end, the book states what an enormous commitment of resources would be needed 'to generate' such an alternative. He points to an alternative faith, not to alternative medicine. I pray he will find it. ' . . . *Faith comes from hearing the message, and the message is heard through the word of Christ*' (Romans 10:17).

The doctor's difficult role

If the drug industry has become the sorcerer, has the doctor become something of a 'sorcerer's apprentice'? Doctors are invariably highly intelligent – they have to be to get through their training – and they have been encouraged to focus on the question, 'does it work?' They are not used to approaching problems 'like a little child' and they are in an extraordinarily difficult situation. On the one hand there are the endless promotions and pressures from the drug companies. On the other they have the demands of an increasing stream of patients; in these days the patients are much less satisfied. Time, patience and solutions are what are really needed, but life has been conditioned by what the drug companies provide. That includes addictive drugs!

Apart from the pharmacology, subject itself to mistakes, when we explore medical science we find that much of it is only theory. A treatment seems to work! It has been tested! So it is repeated! Medicine today is really not as scientific as patients would usually suppose. Consider this up-to-date assessment in a letter written to me by a practising Christian doctor:

> While the medical profession today tries to convince itself that there is a very strong scientific basis for all that we do, particularly with the major advances of technology into the field of medicine, I firmly

believe this to be a total misnomer. When you begin to explore medicine from a totally scientific viewpoint you find vast, and I mean literally vast, areas of physiology and biochemistry which are not understood at all and much of that which is supposedly understood, is at best theory which as we all know constantly changes. Nowhere is this more than in the area of neuro-physiology and neuro-biochemistry which clearly have direct bearing on the psyche. I feel even in this enlightened twentieth century particularly at general practice level, medicine is as much an art as a science. The good doctor and the brilliant scientist are almost invariably not the same person. In the field of general practice to my mind the best practitioners are those who listen, understand and reassure their patients and can, by affecting the patient's attitudes, encourage the inherent healing abilities of the body without recourse to potentially hazardous drugs, whose pharmacology again is often ill understood. Clearly the practitioner must also be aware of that which is illness caused by some pathological process and which indeed can be greatly helped by use of modern drugs and surgical technology, but in my experience this is probably true in less than thirty per cent of cases that a general practitioner will see.

Demons are real; doctors are only human

How has it happened that believers turn to medicine first and to God second? We have been brought up in a scientific age which has deceived us as to true values. Science has bred materialism with a further distance put between us and God. What science has provided have become gods – motor cars, TVs and all the rest. We have come to depend on them. For our health we have likewise focused on medicine. We have made our doctors into god-figures. We have trusted them. We have respected them. We have believed them. We have thought they knew best. We have believed they were bringing science to us through drugs and their skills. Health has been the most important thing to us – at least when we became ill – and we did as the doctor told us. We have leaned too heavily upon him, and now there is a tendency to blame him! When we have treated the doctor as a god, and indeed when he has responded in such a way, we have only ourselves to blame.

Medicine is changing fast

Medicine is a big and complex subject that falls further into the hands of specialists and experts. At the consultant level we have two dozen or more different specialisations in a big hospital. I have little idea of the drugs or the origins of various treatments. Many of us, like the Prince of Wales, sense that all is not right. The swing to 'alternative medicine' is for every kind of reason. In the 1980 Reith Lecture entitled 'Unmasking Medicine', Ian Kennedy, a legal academic, said: 'The practice of medicine has changed. There's a feeling abroad that all may not be well. This feeling grows out of a sense of distance, out of a sense that medicine is in the hands of the experts and sets its own path. We can take it or leave it.'

Science is relatively new and forty years ago prior to penicillin, new really effective medical treatments were quite rare. The change we see in Britain has little to do with the founding of the National Health Service after the Second World War. It is a world that laymen find difficulty in entering and understanding. We receive the drug in the simple form of a pill; yet it is so very complicated. Often it defies all understanding. Indeed a drug can be frighteningly spiritual in its effects.

Apart from hypnotic drugs, hypnotism itself is gaining ground and respectability in the medical profession. There is consultation by doctors of psychics for diagnosis; more doctors are discovering the power in psychic 'healing', being led without realising it deeper into the occult realm.

However most doctors can be trusted. The majority are on the side of science and are not into the spiritual! They are only too pleased when the patient ceases to burden them with the god-like image and when he realises his health is substantially in his own hands.

Our health is our responsibility

Once again the Prince of Wales correctly observed the situation: 'The health of human beings is so often determined by their behaviour, their food and the nature of their environment.'

We have involved our doctors in everything from conception through to the time when they have to write a certificate to say we are dead! As we hook up to drugs we give up part of our sense of responsibility for our own health. We forget that Satan has a powerful vested interest in our ill-health, yet even Christians have neglected the answers to be found in the Bible.

Pointers to the future in the surgery

If we do not have the divine health that was bought for us at Calvary, then there is provided divine healing in the name of Jesus. We have to receive it by faith. Since knowing Jesus I have met brothers and sisters in the Lord who have met the conditions and who walk in divine health in this way. It is recognised that many Christians do not have this level of faith. However there is wonderful provision for our faith, and we find it in the word of God.

Of course God can use doctors and we thank Him for all that is achieved through them. However the conclusion from Scripture must be that the doctor's prescription can only be a second best. Our Lord wants to prove His sufficiency in the area of our health. By His stripes we were healed, and according to His word His sufficiency was always so. The course medicine is assuredly taking today makes our Lord's ways all the more timely for our consideration. 'Why pick on alternative medicine?' was what various doctors asked me when I first embarked on this book. 'What about the state of our own profession?' Yes, indeed!

Many of the drugs are bad enough, but Christians need to be aware that occult alternative therapies appear to be the next step in Satan's plan for the medical profession. Let us take a brief look at the infiltration of blatantly occult alternative therapies into medical science in the United States.

Alternative medicine, whichever way we look at it, has progressed very fast in the past ten years, and the progress is accelerating. It is ten years since it became a recognised subject of teaching in American medical schools. Often teaching will begin with deceptive esoteric technicalities like a description of the human constitution seen in terms of seven states, or levels, of energy. The physical is said to be only the outward manifestation of the lowest form of energy (i.e. matter). The deception runs that in addition to the physical, there are seven more energies that focus on the seven so-called 'chakras' in the body. There is absolutely no scientific basis for the existence of these chakras, and the fact they have been known to occultists for thousands of years doesn't add any credibility to their reality!

The highly regarded John Hopkins Medical School in the United States had opened its door to lecturers in Psychic Healing by 1977*. Whether the classroom is there or in any suburban basement room, what we are told when we probe for an explanation, is that we are in another dimension and that all will become clearer when

* According to *National Enquirer* article: 'Top medical college offers Psychic Healing' (19 July 1977)

171

we reach a higher level of consciousness. People with psychic powers turn out to be the ones who provide the evidence. So far so good; for after all, how could the leading 'brains' in a place like John Hopkins, or Oxford, or Cambridge, fall for all this! The truth is, that in these days there are top scientists who are actually *seeking* these psychic powers. Satan, given an opportunity to lumber us with these powers, will do so; now, many are deliberately seeking these powers to apply to their work in research. Such people are believed to have moved into higher levels of evolution. To give them the assurances they may need, demons can, as they are opened up still further, *show* them the energies they had previously learned about. Satan is a legalist, and once we start on the occult trail, he will be aware of his right to encourage us further. We need to walk in the Spirit with our Lord; not with the devil.

America's student doctors today hear how the initiated are able to bypass the normal process of medical science. One such teacher recently had an audience of some 2,000 to 3,000 people, and an estimated sixty per cent of these, according to a report in the *Spiritual Counterfeits Project Journal* of August 1978, were medical professionals. The teacher, a medical doctor, was speaking on the subject of the 'Dynamics of the Etheric-Astral-Mental Fields in the Healing Process'. He saw the future in this way: 'The medical model of the future is one in which a "sensitive" with higher perception is involved with both diagnosis and treatment.' The reality would be diagnosis and treatment in the hands of demons. The warning is worth repeating: we can no longer afford to ignore the spiritual status of those who minister to us whether in the surgery or in the church.

While more and more doctors enthusiastically go looking for solutions in the spiritual dimension, the vast majority, whether in Britain or in America, busy doing their jobs as well as they can understand them, pay little regard to these alternatives. However, the trend in self-help is not only opening patients to the ideas of alternative medicine; the self-help movement is bringing patients into a different dialogue with doctors. Doctors will learn from their patients! This apart, the doctor is seen much less as a god figure by younger people; the younger doctor has been opened already to the new thinking.

In a recent book* published by the World Health Organisation, we are told something about this trend in self-help:

> We are witness to a reorientation in health care provision which might prove as fundamental in the long run as the rise of the medical profession 150 years ago. The key word that symbolises this development is self-help . . . Self-help encompasses both self-help groups, self-help organisations and alternative care, all of which are part of what as a phenomenon has been referred to as the Self-Help Movement.

The WHO book contains a description of one Patients' Association in England. From the full account given it is clear the relationships between patients and doctors will have benefited. However, and as the WHO Introduction quoted above indicates, self-help incorporates both alternative therapies and these groups. This Patients' Association has had 'about nine evening meetings each year' trying to 'keep a balance between specialist subjects (heart disease, arthritis, acupuncture, marriage counselling) and more general preventive medicine (eating and health problems of old age, knowing your pills and potions)', and we read that, as a result of the 'talk on yoga' there have been weekly classes for members of the practice for the past three years.

We know that if we keep our eyes open we see there

* *Self-Help and Health in Europe* (WHO – Regional Office for Europe) – 1983

173

are talks on yoga followed by yoga classes held in many different places. However the concern here must be with the overtures Satan is making, not only in encouraging the out-and-out searchers amongst the doctors, but also to the hardheaded, hard worked general practitioner who has neither the time nor inclination to go to lectures on subjects like 'Dynamics of the Etheric-Astral-Mental Fields in the Healing Process'.

There are more ways than one of getting yoga, acupuncture and all the rest closer, and then *into,* the surgery of every doctor. Patients' associations and self-help groups seem to be one more way. The idea of these groups is good. As ever, Satan much prefers to work through something that is good.

Satan has his answers all ready

Satan – the planner – is ready. He says, 'You have looked outside of yourself for the answer, and you haven't found it in science and drugs'. So now he says, 'Look to yourself for the answer. It's very simple. The answer was there all the time. The ancient peoples understood it. But you've been too busy with science'. 'Look at the natural things' he would say to us. 'Look to homoe-opathy with its herbs and its minerals! Go to work on those energy lines in your body that even the ancient Chinese could understand! Look at the psychic powers you can develop!' What Satan doesn't whisper is that drugs have helped prepare our spirits for the 'alternative medicine' scene. We have been conditioned for a reaction to the wonder drugs. Now the emphasis is shifting to so-called natural mixtures and potions; going deeper than just the symptoms; practitioners with more time to spare; the 'whole person' treatment; diet, exercise and personal responsibility; no side-effects – a carefully prepared mixture of the counterfeit and the beneficial with just about the right dosage in line with what the patient will take.

A born again rector of a busy parish put it this way in a letter to me:

The pressures on doctors to cope with demands on them means they can only give each patient an average six minutes each! Hence people's dissatisfaction with orthodox medicine has turned them to those who will give them what they really want (they think!) which is more time for someone to treat them as a person and not a number. So often the people filling this gap are precisely those outlined (referring to the sort of therapies seen in Part Two). Hence the need for Christians to lead people to find that sense of wholeness and self-value which is only ours through the love of God the Father revealed in the Son Jesus Christ and lived in the power of the Holy Spirit. Physical healing is only a very small part of what we need. 'By His stripes we are healed'.

Healing is to be found in Jesus. Against that, man is being wooed by the powers of darkness in 'alternative medicine'. There is spiritual warfare, and Satan's 'simple' answer is the counterfeit of the most simple answer of all – to receive the wholeness and life that Jesus died to give us.

20: Moral Rearmament health conference

I sent out one hundred letters and trusted I would be covered by prayer as I attended a Health Care Conference promoted by Moral Rearmament, in Switzerland. The time was spiritually debilitating much as I anticipated, but it had seemed to be right that I go.

I had been to one previous World Assembly of MRA, but this would be my only visit as a born again believer. Would I really find any born again people there? Would I find any believers to whom I could relate in the medical field? How would I find MRA now that I knew Jesus, now I knew that He was the Healer?

I found *many* born again believers. Furthermore many of them were seeking so evidently actually to *live* moral lives, the sort of lives they had found generally lacking in many of the traditional churches they had known. However there were many at the conference who will never have heard the gospel of Jesus.

Since its foundation, I believe the movement was taken out of balance by its focus on the absolute moral standards of love, honesty, unselfishness and purity, rather than on the person of Jesus. Certainly I found no focus on Jesus in 1984.

Unlike my visit three years earlier, being now a Christian, I was sensitive to much that was led by the spirit of Antichrist and the New Age. One lovely born again man whom I knew from previous meetings, to reinforce a point he was making to me, said 'We should ask the tree before we cut it down.' Another asked me, 'Why does God need you to go laying hands on people?'

The Dalai Lama was quoted approvingly by the

British general practitioner who opened the conference. The Tibetan Buddhist leader was at that time touring Britain and being widely received by church leaders as a spokesman for ecumenism and religious tolerance. More significantly in the New Age, there can be seen in the Dalai Lama a missionary zeal that is both subtle and unexpected from the eastern religions. This **Buddhist** spiritual leader was the president of the 1979 World **Hindu** Conference. Ecumenism and compromise are not only gaining ground in the west, but in the east too.

At the same introductory session we were encouraged by a Moslem, 'Don't fall into the trap of seeing only one God.' Everything but the Bible seemed to be quoted. 'We all have this priceless gift of inner intelligence,' the speaker said. Another platform speaker said, 'I was scientific, then I discovered the writings of old doctors.' 'The great doctor, Paracelsus,' didn't of course escape the conference's mention. I heard another say, 'We are one family at this conference, breathing through one another,' but this was not the Christian conference I am familiar with where there is a unity that comes from the focus of all on Jesus.

This movement seemed to have deteriorated by a long stretch since Frank Buchman founded it as the Oxford Group following upon his conversion at the Keswick Convention more than fifty years previously. As ever Satan built upon what was good. Still he works on that principle today. 'In my religion abortion is strictly forbidden,' one of the principal speakers told us. 'This gives me a completely new view and respect for Islam,' was the reply of one well respected speaker, and when the distinguished Muslim was seated, a medical doctor from Canada, whom I knew, led the large assembly in a standing ovation. Dr Campbell was a principal speaker too. He was the former doctor of Frank Buchman. He was also the joint author of *Remaking Men*.

I had fellowshipped mostly with the Hindus, who were much in evidence, at the previous conference. Perhaps it was a sign of the times that the principal contributor at this conference (made up of entirely orthodox medical personnel rather than those from the alternative therapies) was an Egyptian from oil-rich Kuwait. The doctor hadn't given us anything from the Bible, but the medical professor from the University of Kuwait, and whose idea the conference was, gave us quotations from the Koran. Here was a really attractive man with peace, morality and kindness shining out from him, and it was his job to address us on 'Moral and Ethical Issues.' But he didn't know that Jesus Christ was the only way to the Father.

As I observe the resolute way in which believers and others, whether in their own strengths or in any other way, live by these attractive moral standards, and how they influence the lives of others, I see how subtle it is, and how easy it can be to stray when we take our eyes off Jesus. My thoughts turned to the wider New Age scene as the religions and cults like MRA prepare the ground for the peace, unity and supernatural power that the world is seeking. It is not the unity of believers, nor that peace that passes all understanding. It is the peace that the world and the cults can give, and the power promises to be the power of the occult.

All of the speakers were orthodox medical men and women, and it was a Swiss psychiatrist, who stirred the most approval with what seemed to be a confused mixture of psychiatry, theology and the occult. The contents were the ingredients so readily recognised by those who are at all familiar with Satan's ways in these days: ' . . . he should practise the maximum possible physical and mental inactivity . . . composure, Maryan openness, and self-critical humility towards the workings of God's grace.' Jesus came to give life and we are not to be left wide open to demon activity by this sort of meditative contemplation. Jesus came so that we can have a real relationship with Him, and not listen to the repetitive and rhythmic prayers the professor described as part of his treatments.

Another therapy this psychiatrist had developed was what he called, 'a three year course of prayer in basic psychosomatic therapy.' He concluded: 'I have often found that people who have finished their final period of three years' therapy do not want to give up the searching, transforming, praying and thanking way to God.' His observation is correct! But we search at our peril! They *may* find their way to God. The only way is through Jesus. No search is necessary. Jesus is just a prayer away!

The MRA Health Care Conference made a small yet significant contribution to New Age health care. Orthodox medical practitioners were discovering there *is* a spiritual way. Yet the only spiritual way they dare take is the way that is with Jesus, *'for false Christs and false prophets will appear and perform great signs and miracles to deceive even the elect – if that were possible. See I have told you ahead of time.'* (Matthew 24: 24–25)

21: The Bible's medical answers

The Bible has given doctors the answers in the past

Before looking at the health that can be ministered to us in the name of Jesus in Chapter Twenty-two, let us see the contribution the Bible makes into the area of preventive medicine. S I McMillen MD, in *None of these Diseases** relates how the Black Death was brought under control. He tells us that in the fourteenth century alone this killer disease took the lives of one in four people, an estimated total of sixty million. Then the church set about separating the afflicted according to God's word in Leviticus 13: 46: '*As long as he has the infection he remains unclean. He must live alone; he must live outside the camp.*'

We can take a look back at the nineteenth century when there were epidemics of cholera and typhoid through the dumping of human excrement in the streets. God promised Moses that the Israelites in Egypt would have none of these diseases (Exodus 15: 26). However there was something *they* had to do and it was written in Deuteronomy 23: 12–13: '*Designate a place outside the camp where you can go to relieve yourself. As part of your equipment have something to dig with, and when you relieve yourself, dig a hole and cover up your excrement.*' Could the Lord have made it any plainer? However He was ignored by the grand designers in places like Florence

---

* Published by Marshall, Morgan & Scott – 1966

and Vienna where there was little concern for the open sewers.

The Bible today

The Bible is a supernatural book, always providing the answer; practical and up-to-date. More and more are devoted to the counterfeit answers provided by horoscopes, but for increasing numbers with eyes to see and ears to hear, the Bible gives the only truth that can be found. Today alcohol is a major killer and the word of God contains the truth about it. Proverbs 23: 31–32 says: *'Do not gaze at wine when it is red, when it sparkles in the cup, when it goes down smoothly! In the end it bites like a snake and poisons like a viper.'*

Lung cancer and coronary heart disease, both brought on by smoking, are major killers. We have all seen medical pictures of lungs destroyed by inhaled smoke. In 1 Corinthians 6: 19 we can read: *'Do you not know that your body is a temple of the Holy Spirit, who is in you, whom you have received from God? You are not your own; you were bought at a price. Therefore honour God with your body.'*

Venereal disease, little discussed in 'polite society', is nonetheless a prevalent and most dreadful disease. Proverbs 5: 3–5 has this to say: *'For the lips of an adulteress drip honey, and her speech is smoother than oil; but in the end she is bitter as gall, sharp as a double-edged sword. Her feet go down to death; her steps lead straight to the grave.'*

And what of our minds, diseased through following our own inclinations and not allowing the Holy Spirit to provide the essential love, joy and peace? Paul told the Galatians what any good doctor would suggest we avoid to promote good physical and mental health. Galatians 5: 19–21 says: *'The acts of a sinful nature are obvious: sexual immorality, impurity and debauchery; idolatry and witchcraft; hatred, discord, jealousy, fits of rage, selfish*

181

ambition, dissensions, factions and envy; drunkenness, orgies and the like.' Satan is the author of the psychosomatic disorders that are brought about through these sinful acts, and these disorders amount, according to general practitioners, for some seventy per cent or so of the patients coming to them.

Psychosomatic disorders

The Bible has much to say about Satan, the source of occult power and the author of disease. We have seen that he is the power behind many alternative healing methods. Often he is the power behind accidents and much else besides. He is the enemy encouraging the sinful nature that gives rise to the majority of bodily afflictions. Satan works on the human mind, and this is where the psychosomatic illness originates, where doctors find no pathology or tissue disease. How then can Christians deal with Satan when he makes a personal attack?

We need to know Satan

In one sense I knew Satan and his power through my 'search' into alternative medicine, and before I knew Jesus as my Saviour and Lord. I believe many spend twenty years or so going to church – as I did – before really **knowing** Jesus. Then, for need of teaching and because Satan blinds, they can easily spend another twenty years and still not **know** Satan. The enemy is not 'evil'. The enemy is a personality – Satan.

Isn't it better not to think about the enemy? Satan himself plants that question in many minds. When our soldiers were doing battle against Germany in Europe, they weren't concentrating on the evil of Nazi philosophy and of Hitler, but on the enemy that confronted them. Like them, Christians have a battle on their hands and we have to **know** the enemy. The Bible tells us in Ephesians 6: 12 that our battle is not against flesh and blood but against Satan's spiritual forces. In the battle against Hitler, our leaders had to understand his tactics as best they could, and our military officers took account of them on the battle field. In the battle against Satan we can know his tactics because the Bible reveals them to us.

The Bible says that Satan attacks viciously (1 Peter 5: 8). He takes advantage of human weakness (2 Cor. 2: 11), and he blinds our spiritual vision (2 Cor. 4: 4). He seeks to bind us physically, mentally and spiritually (Luke 13: 16; Acts 10: 38). Satan is a counterfeiter (Acts 8: 9–11), who deceives all men (Rev. 12: 9; 2 Cor. 11: 14ff). He hinders the gospel (2 Thess. 2: 7–10); he steals the truth (Matt. 13: 19; John 10: 10); he afflicts and destroys (Job 2: 3–6; John 10: 10); he is a liar and can't be trusted (Acts 5: 3; 1 John 2: 22). Satan's demons can indwell both humans and animals (Matt. 8: 31ff). Satan accuses humanity, and Christians in particular (Zech. 3). He tempts all to sin (Luke 22: 31; Matt. 16: 22ff), and he is interested in governments too (Dan. 10: 10–13; 12: 1; Rev. 13).

Jesus has already won the victory on the cross, and He is with us in our battles. However *we* do the fighting. We need to get light focused on the enemy, heed what God says about him and not be afraid to talk to others about him. We need to have a healthy respect for him. We are much safer when we know him as Jesus knew him, and in the light of what God says about him.

We need to watch out for Satan

He seeks to inspire in us the wickedness so well summarised in the letter of Paul to the Galatians already referred to in this chapter. Accordingly we have to watch out for him. *'Watch and pray so that you will not fall into temptation. The spirit is willing but the body is weak'* (Matthew 26: 41).

Satan is at work in the area of our health. We have seen that he is at work in the area of alternative medicine. There is not one of his tactics referred to above that he could not use in these areas, but we can be ready for him when he first puts that sinful thought into our minds or when we first start to doubt God's word. In his book, *Dealing with the Devil**, C S Lovett sets out valuable steps for dealing with one personal weakness at a time. This is a practical book for those who mean business with Satan and it was a great help to me, pointing to the need to recognise his attack.

The attack might be a worry or a fear, a thought of dissatisfaction, gossip or laziness, a jealous idea, a feeling of pride, or, in the context of health, a doubt that our Lord is the Lord who heals us (Exodus 15: 26) and who carried our diseases in His own body so that we don't have to bear them (Matthew 8: 17). The list, encouraged by Satan and forbidden by God, is a long one, but the Holy Spirit always dwells within us and we can allow ourselves to be led by Him.

With practice, at the onset of a thought, we can instantly submit ourselves to God by speaking to Him. Then, in His presence, we can fearlessly address Satan **in the name of Jesus:** 'Devil, get out of my mind, in Jesus' name. I won't even entertain such thoughts. By my Lord's stripes I am healed.' Then, having done everything, 'to stand'. *'Submit yourselves, then, to God. Resist the devil, and he will flee from you. Come near to God and he will come near to you.'* (James 4: 7–8) The word says 'he will flee from you' and, in due time, he does.

---

* Published by Personal Christianity Chapel, Box 549, Baldwin Park, CA 91706, USA

The weapon is the word of God

Meditation on the word of God, which drove Satan away, is good for keeping him at a distance once he is gone. In that way as we 'come near to God he will come near to us.' Satan says 'Worry about it!'. The Christian replies, 'It is written, be anxious for nothing . . .' Satan says, 'That disease will come back.' The Christian replies, 'By His stripes I am healed! Be gone, in Jesus' name.' We have to do it God's way, according to His word: *'For though we live in the world we do not wage war as the world does. The weapons we fight with are not the weapons of the world. On the contrary, they have divine power to demolish strongholds. We demolish arguments and every pretension that sets itself up against the knowledge of God, and we take captive every thought to make it obedient to Christ.'* (2 Corinthians 10: 3–5)

Thus an important 'Medical Answer' from the Bible is to deal with Satan, the author of the disease. The battles against Satan are *our* battles. We are told how to fight. Some battles have to be repeated, but they get fewer as we tackle them God's way.

PART FIVE
DIVINE HEALING: A
SCRIPTURAL GUIDE

22: God's prescription

Jesus has already paid the price

Jesus suffered every disease in His own body so that we would not have to bear them. ' . . . *there were many who were appalled at him – his appearance was so disfigured beyond that of any man and his form marred beyond human likeness. . . . he was pierced for our transgressions, he was crushed for our iniquities; the punishment that brought us peace was upon him, and by his wounds we are healed.'* (Is. 52:14; 53:5) This is what the prophet Isaiah wrote, 700 years before God sent His Son Jesus to live on the earth as a man. Jesus died so that we can be forgiven our sins. The Bible also says *'He bore our diseases in His body that we might be healed'*. He offers us salvation from our sins. He offers us healing. The same word *sozo* in the Greek includes salvation *and* the healing of our bodies.

'Jesus Christ is the same yesterday, today and forever.' (Heb 13:8) Jesus lived in the days of Isaiah and He lives today. He saves those that receive him today. He still heals today. *'This was to confirm what was spoken through the prophet Isaiah: "He took up our infirmities and carried our diseases".'* (Matt 8:17)

The truth

The truth is in God's word. That is what Satan, the **deceiver,** seeks to steal from us. Once he can do that – once he can get us away from hearing and believing the

187

truth of God's word – sickness, death and much more besides can follow, but it is we who have given that power to him by taking our eyes off God and His word. **We** have been given the power to 'trample on snakes and scorpions (evil spirits) and to overcome all the power of the enemy (Satan)' (Luke 10: 19)

Satan purposes, through deception, to steal, kill and destroy, but **he** doesn't have the power to do these things. When John wrote of the thief who 'comes only to kill and steal and destroy' (John 10: 10) he is not referring to Satan but to false prophets and false shepherds. Satan can only deceive through our minds and emotions. We neglect God's word on divine health. We soon forget that Jesus suffered every disease in His own body so that we don't have to bear them. If we do get sick we are most often not in a state of faith where we can believe God wants us to receive our healing according to any of the ways which He provides for us to do so. That is because we allow Satan to deceive us just as he is deceiving many of the practitioners in alternative medicine. We give Satan the power when we start to look at our circumstances, feelings, and at the ways of the world. We need to look at what God says.

Once again, what do we find in God's word about healing and health? Peter confirmed what Isaiah wrote, and what Matthew wrote. Peter wrote what God still says: *'He himself bore our sins in his body on the tree, so that we might die to sins and live for righteousness; by his wounds you have been healed.'* (1 Peter 2: 24) When we allow Satan to steal the truth from us we don't see much healing. The truth is only to be found in God's word. That truth is something greater than the mere evidence this world can provide.

The truth tells us that Satan is a defeated foe. Jesus defeated him at Calvary and we can believe in Him who died for our sins and sicknesses. He died to take the authority from Satan. Satan had stolen it from Adam by deception, and now it is handed back to those who will believe and walk in faith according to the truth of God's word.

Salvation and divine health: both by faith

Jesus has already suffered for us, but we cannot expect to receive healing until we **receive** Him and **know** Him. Many believe in Jesus but He is not real to them. They have not received Him and they do not know Him. They do not see that He is true to His word in the Bible. '*Yet to all who received him, to those who believed in his name, he gave the right to become children of God – children born not of natural descent, nor of human decision, but born of God.*' (John 1: 12–13) I believe the Lord will speak to those who don't know Jesus through the message in Chapter Twenty-five.

As believers we often accept Jesus as the Healer, but when, after much prayer, we see no change, we look at our circumstances rather than to the truth of God's word. The truth is stolen from us. Let Jesus speak for himself: '*If you remain in me, and my words remain in you, ask whatever you wish, and it will be given to you. This is to my Father's glory, that you bear much fruit, showing yourselves to be my disciples.*' (John 15: 7–8) The thief who steals the word (John 10:10) wants the glory to go to Satan. He wants us to believe his lies. He wants us to believe that God won't heal us. He wants us to believe that Jesus hasn't already paid the price for us.

If God's word remains in us, we shall believe for our healing. We shall have faith for our healing. Once we have received Jesus as our Saviour, Lord and Healer, faith becomes the essence of our relationship with Him. The Bible tells us how to receive that faith: '*Faith comes from hearing the message, and the message is heard through the word of Christ.*' (Romans 10:17) Faith and the word go together. In these days we need the Scriptures on health and healing written in our hearts.

A closer look at Calvary health

Any look at health Scriptures must begin at Calvary: Jesus suffered every disease in his own body so that we would not have to bear them. That truth is so important; Satan so often steals it from us! It is right to put emphasis on it as we do on all that Jesus did for us at Calvary.

Matthew 8: 17 is a clear statement about sickness. *'He took up our infirmities and carried our diseases.'* However, Isaiah 53: 4 appears to be less helpful. It is worth a closer look in the Hebrew: 'Surely he took up (*nasa*) our infirmities (*kholee*) and carried (*sabal*) our sorrows (*makob*)'. *Nasa* appears to mean 'bear', or 'bore' in the sense of suffering punishment for something. The same word is used in Leviticus 5: 1, 'he will be held responsible'; or, in the AV, 'bear'. *Kholee* appears to mean 'sicknesses', from *chalah* (to be weak, sick or afflicted). In Deuteronomy 7: 15 ('The Lord will keep you free from every disease') we have the same word *kholee*.

Surely then, Jesus suffered the punishment for our sins, not only by shedding His blood to save us from the consequences of our sins, but **also** by the **sicknesses** that He bore for us. We can believe God for our salvation. However, Satan, the flesh, so-called medical science, and the rest of the circumstances that are of this world, keep pressing in on us until we doubt the truth of God's word on divine health (assuming Satan hasn't already kept these Scriptures from us anyway!)

So much for the 'infirmities' or 'sicknesses'. What about where the NIV tells us Jesus 'carried' (*sabal*) our 'sorrows' (*makob*)? *Sabal* seems to mean 'bore' in the way of a penalty or chastisement. In Lamentations 5: 7 we read that we bear (*sabal*) the punishment of our fathers' sins. Then at Calvary, Jesus 'bore' the penalty – *sabal* again. The penalty to be borne is the pains. *Makob* seems to mean 'pains' – physical pains. In Job 33: 19 we read: 'On a bed of pain (*makob*) with constant distress in his bones'. That speaks of physical pain.

Surely then Jesus didn't only bear the sicknesses that Satan seeks to inflict on us to stop our bodies working properly. He also bore the physical pains that so often accompany these sicknesses.

Jesus is into the healing of our **physical** bodies! He is into getting rid of our **physical** pains. In 1 Peter 2: 24 ('by his wounds you have been healed') the Greek word *iaomai* is used, and it seems that, without exception, in the New Testament this is, always and only, applied to physical healing.

Jesus was always the healer

Jesus healed all our sicknesses even before He himself became the sacrifice under the New Covenant. God gave Moses a remarkable promise for the new nation of Israel. He said: *'If you listen carefully to the voice of the Lord your God and do what is right in his eyes, if you pay attention to his commands and keep all his decrees, I will not bring on you any of the diseases I brought on the Egyptians, for I am the Lord that heals you.'* (Exodus 15: 26)

Psalm 103: 3 says: 'He forgives all my sins and heals all my diseases,' and, again in Exodus, we read: *'Worship the Lord your God, and his blessing will be on your food and water. I will take away sickness from among you, and none will miscarry or be barren in your land. I will give you a full life-span.'*

Jesus is the same yesterday, today and forever. How much easier should it be under the New Covenant to see our sicknesses gone and a full life span – if only we will believe God rather than the world or Satan? God is sufficient on His own to meet the health needs of all who will believe Him.

Faith comes by hearing the word of God

He is gentle with us as we grow in Him. However the speed at which we grow is entirely up to us. It is according to the measure of our faith in God. Without faith it is impossible to please God (Hebrews 11: 6). Faith comes only from the revelation of His supernatural word. What better prescription then for the sick than health Scriptures, health Scriptures and more health Scriptures! Faith in God for health comes from God's word on health. (Romans 10: 17)

Before pulling together more Scriptures on healing and health, two points should be emphasised. Firstly, if we don't keep coming back to Isaiah 53: 4–5, the truth that Jesus suffered every disease and pain in His own body so that we would not have to bear them, we can very soon lose sight of what was done at Calvary. Secondly, there is ample provision in Scripture for praying for the sick to be healed, but it is surely better to get the revelation that we **are healed** (*sozo*) and live in divine health. We have the revelation that we **are saved** (*sozo*). The word is the same. Jesus saw no difference: '*Which is easier: to say, "Your sins are forgiven", or to say, "Get up and walk"?*' (Matthew 9: 4) Why don't we believe that sin and sickness go together and that Jesus dealt with both?

Remembering our Lord's body

Jesus never said it would be easy but He did help us in this way:

> '*This is my body, which is for you; do this in remembrance of me.*' *In the same way, after supper he took the cup, saying, 'This cup is the new covenant in my blood; do this, whenever you drink it, in remembrance of me.' For whenever you eat this bread and drink this cup, you proclaim the Lord's death until he comes. Therefore, whoever eats the bread or drinks the cup of the Lord in an unworthy manner will be guilty of sinning against the body and blood of the Lord. A man ought to examine himself before he eats of the*

bread and drinks of the cup. For anyone who eats and drinks without recognising the body of the Lord eats and drinks judgment on himself. That is why many among you are weak and sick and a number of you have fallen asleep. (1 Corinthians 11: 24–30)

Our Lord is helping us, but He is also sounding a warning! Paul gives us one reason why many are sick: anyone who eats and drinks without recognising (*diakrinon*) the body of the Lord, eats and drinks judgment (sickness or whatever) on himself.

The Greek word *Diakrinon* appears to mean 'making a distinction between', and Paul is pointing out to the Corinthians in the above Scripture, the distinction between the bread and the wine. When we take communion we need to remember the difference between them. Paul urges us to remember that Jesus **did** bear our sicknesses and pains. His body was broken for them and this is quite different and distinct from His blood, shed to save us from the eternal consequences of our sins.

His body was 'marred beyond human likeness' (Is. 52: 14) through bearing our sicknesses and pains. As Jesus taught us, we eat the bread to remind us of that. We need to **understand** the Scripture before we can be reminded! Alas Satan can steal enough of the truth from us so that we miss the whole truth. Even large numbers of Bible-believing Christians miss it. We forget the distinction between the bread and the wine. Once again, in the Old Testament, most of us remember the blood of the lamb that the Israelites had to put 'on the sides and tops of the door frames of the houses' (Exodus 12: 7). More easily we forget the requirement 'that same night they are to eat the meat . . .' (Exodus 12: 8).

Faith in God: Satan is a liar

As Christians we have our salvation. It includes healing! Why should we settle for anything less? We don't have to allow Satan to steal this truth from us. More and more Christians are coming to the place in these days where they are willing to make a 100 per cent surrender to God. When we have faith and are ready, God is ready. When, as an act of faith, we start weaning ourselves off pills and potions, when we really start believing God's word rather than doctors' prognoses, and when we turn from the answers the world gives to the solutions our Father has for us, then He will be ready to meet us.

We can have the necessary faith in God for our health by not doubting His word in our heart. Meditating on the word of God on health can soon get the message firmly written in our hearts. Satan will be at work to try to stop us in the apparently straightforward business of meditating on the healing Scriptures. After all Satan's purpose is to bring physical and spiritual death to all of us. Acts 10: 38 tells us how sickness is the devil's work: ' . . . *he* (Jesus) *went around doing good and healing all who were under the power of the devil, because God was with him.*' Most often death comes in this way – Satan's way. Satan is the author of sin, sickness and death! He is the ruler of this world.

Disease and death are from Satan

When we were born again, we received resurrection life; thereafter Jesus' life is our example. He suffered and died for us at Calvary. He knew perfectly well it was His Father's will that **He** should die on the cross for us. It can never be the Father's will that **we** should die of disease at the hand of Satan when Jesus has already paid the price of sin for us. It is absurd that Christians should follow Jesus' example and, in the face of **Satan's** threats of death, pray as Jesus did in the Garden of Gethsemane.

Physical death from disease is from Satan. Jesus came 'that they might have life, and have it to the full' (John 10: 10). Needless to say, to be sick or to die is not a sin! Let it be said too that our Lord is most certainly able to bring blessings out of the situations Satan brings about. However it seems perfectly clear from the word that such sickness and death cannot at the same time come from Satan *and* be glorifying to the Lord. We can be impressed by the way that Christians bear their suffering – and rightly so – but before we start eulogising some of the fine Christians that have been cut down in their prime, let us realise that only God knew their heart. Consider whether they really had the revelation of God's word in the area of health and healing!

Healing evangelists will say that many are healed through their own faith by meditating on health and healing Scriptures, however they received them, or read them. The important parts of these health and healing chapters are the Scriptures themselves. We need to be convinced beyond any doubt that God wants us well. We are convinced of our salvation; both come through knowing what God's word declares.

God's word, not man's evidence

God's word is God's prescription for life and health. *'My son, pay attention to what I say; listen closely to my words. Do not let them out of your sight, keep them within your heart; for they are life to those who find them and health to a man's whole body. Above all else guard your heart, for it is the wellspring of life.'* (Proverbs 4: 20–23)

The truth about a patient's health is to be found in the health Scriptures. What good is it when, after visiting a sick brother or sister, we report a situation that is contrary to God's word? In fact, it is harmful.

When Moses sent twelve men to explore Canaan they brought back a bad report (Numbers 13: 32). The AV calls it an 'evil' report. It was an evil report because it did not measure up to the word of God. It was a lie of Satan that the giants were stronger than the twelve. The Israelites believed the lie. They asked Moses: 'Wouldn't it be better for us to go back to Egypt?' (Numbers 14: 3). God wants us to know the truth of His word now, just as He did then. Are we more interested in x-rays, the doctors' prognoses and the patients' pains and feelings, than in what God has to say about it?

Satan would swing us right out of balance in the face of illness: 'You agree with the patient! *He's* the one that's got to suffer it; who are *you* to talk?' In one sense Satan is right when he whispers that. Satan is often 'nearly right' but we can, with confidence, speak God's word.

The Lord put it this way: *'Cursed is the one who trusts in man, who depends on flesh for his strength and whose heart turns away from the Lord. He will be like a bush in the wastelands; he will not see prosperity when it comes. He will dwell in the parched places of the desert, in a salt land where no-one lives. But blessed is the man who trusts in the Lord, whose confidence is in him.'* (Jeremiah 17: 5–7) We can hardly have faith for divine healing when our trust is really in man. In these days it is humanism that exalts man in the belief that man's abilities can solve human problems. In line with this philosophy for our health we trust the research worker, the scientist, the drug company, the NHS, the experimenters (baboon heart transplants and such like), the doctor, the chemist, and so on.

I wish to bring no condemnation of these groups of people who seek to solve our health problems through the learning that has come their way. But don't let us pretend it is God's way! Don't let's confuse the recovery man can certainly bring by his own efforts, with God's way – the Bible way. Harold Horton, one of the Pentecostal pioneers, put it this way: 'Has the Lord really given over his beloved sick to the world, and His precious Gifts of Healings to the ungodly who reject His grace daily and even blaspheme His holy name?'. *'Blessed is*

196

*the man who trusts in the Lord, whose confidence is in him.
He will be like a tree planted by the water that sends out its
roots by the stream. It does not fear when heat comes; its
leaves are always green. It has no worries in a year of
drought and never fails to bear fruit.'* (Jeremiah 17: 7–8)

Hear the Holy Spirit and not the deceiver

Satan brings sickness, then death, through his power to
deceive us. Death through sickness or accident is not
from God. Once Satan gets us away from the word of
God, he can soon have us believing the wrong thing.
Whilst we sometimes see God turning Satan's schemes
upside down, when people, in the midst of their sickness,
start to believe their troubles are making them stronger,
they are inviting more of Satan's dirty tricks. Many fine
Christians seem to think Satan and his sicknesses are
preparing them for works of service! The word of God
and the Holy Spirit, together with the apostles, prophets,
evangelists, pastors and teachers (Ephesians 4: 11) are
God's provision in this area!

God can use Satan; we must not. In no sense is it
God's will that we lose our health or our peace; indeed
it is God's will that we receive it back again immediately.

Jesus has paid the price. God didn't let Satan into our
health situation; we did. We have the authority, the
armour (Ephesians 6: 14–18) and the free will. We can
stick with the word of God and the Holy Spirit that
indwells every born again believer, or we can grant credibility to the whispers of Satan as he seeks to keep us in
our sicknesses after giving them to us in the first place.

God's mercy

It is good to know something about the person in whom
we put our faith for our healing! We can know from our
Father's word what He says about Himself. That is

better than our own ideas, and we find that He is a God of mercy.

> ' . . . *merciful and gracious, long-suffering, and abundant in goodness and truth.*' (Exodus 34: 6 AV)

> '*Let them now that fear the Lord say, that his mercy endureth for ever.*' (Psalm 118: 4 AV)

> '*For we have not a high priest which cannot be touched with the feeling of our infirmities; but was in all points tempted like as we are, yet without sin. Let us therefore come boldly into the throne of grace, that we may obtain mercy, and find grace to help in time of need.*' (Hebrews 4: 15–16 AV)

We need to *know* from the word that our God is a God of mercy. We have to *confess* the word (Psalm 118: 4), *act* on the word, and boldly come to the place where we can *receive* His mercy (Hebrews 4: 16). Praise the Lord! His mercy endures forever.

Vital Bible knowledge

To avoid sickness and death we need God's *wisdom* (foolish though this may seem in the face of medical science) and the *knowledge* that God has provided (Proverbs 2: 6; Hosea 4: 6).

We must know from God's word – without any shadow of doubt – that it is God's will that we receive our healing. '*But when he asks, he must believe and not doubt, because he who doubts is like a wave of the sea, blown and tossed by the wind. That man should not think he will receive anything from the Lord; he is a double-minded man, unstable in all he does.*' (James 1: 6–8). We cannot reap the harvest of healing without first planting the seed. The first thing is to know it is God's will to heal us. There is no basis for expecting a harvest if we don't have the **faith** in God that He will honour His word. This positive faith is very different from positive thinking, the counterfeit in the alternative treatments of illness in these days.

Concentration on the word of God is not ignoring the problem. Faith in God is acting in the knowledge that victory is certain. Using God's word we speak the answers on which faith and men's hearts can be built. The word of God is sharper than any two-edged sword (Hebrews 4: 12), so let us use it to **disarm** the problem. We don't ignore it. However the word says that no *man* can tame the tongue (James 3: 8), so let us realise its ability carelessly to curse (James 3: 10). Patient and visitor – let's be careful what we say and what we receive! Let us give our tongues over to God.

Sickness has already been bound in heaven. Satan, using deception, works through man's physical body to rule and to destroy, but it is man who is given the authority on earth. Jesus tells us He will give us the keys of the Kingdom of heaven: *'Whatever you bind on earth will be bound in heaven, and whatever you loose on earth will be loosed in heaven.'* (Matthew 16: 19)

Jesus has won the victory over Satan on the cross. Satan remains the ruler of this world, but those who know Jesus are in God's kingdom. We still need to know Satan, to put on the armour of God, and to fight him. *'We do not wage war as the world does . . . they* (the weapons) *have the divine power to demolish strongholds.'* (2 Corinthians 10: 3–4)

The disease curse is lifted

Jesus took the curse (the penalty) of sin and bore it on the cross. The curse of the law included diseases (Deuteronomy 28: 21) but we have to appropriate what Christ has done. We don't any longer have to accept the curse of the law; we have to believe that Jesus bore it for us. He has redeemed us from the curse of the law

(Galatians 3: 1). When we are born again we have the authority to use Jesus' name. However, we still have to take action. God expects us to deal with Satan and his demons. Having submitted ourselves to God, and resisted the devil in Jesus' name, we can expect him to flee from us. We can then draw nearer to God by praying God's will according to his word (James 4: 7–8).

Thus as we seek to be free of our sicknesses, another truth Satan seeks to steal from us is that we have to address him in Jesus' name. When we have Jesus living in us by His Spirit, whether we are laying hands on the sick or whether we are addressing Satan and his demons in Jesus' name, Jesus is right there with us. He wants to have this supreme place in our lives.

The armour and the sword

We have the power in Jesus to bind Satan (Matthew 12: 29) – a good thing to do at least at the start of each day! Also we need to see that our lives are held together by the truth of God's word, 'the belt of truth'. We need to **know** who we are in Christ Jesus. Our lives need to be right with God and right with others. We can **know** that we are sons and that we are worthy. We need to feel secure, rather than feeling like worms! We will have on our 'breastplate of righteousness'. It seems an excellent thing to put on the belt, the breastplate and the 'boots of the gospel of peace' every day. We have a gospel of peace. When we have that peace we are standing ready to be used by God.

As for the rest of the armour in Ephesians 6, if we are in the thick of the fight all the time, then we need the rest of it all the time. Especially first thing in the morning, we can be attacked in our imagination. The shield of faith involves putting trust in God, praising God and turning to His word. The helmet of salvation is our knowledge that we are saved and healed. The sword of the spirit is what we have to fight with. We **use** the word of God to drive away demons – from ourselves and from others. We address Satan and he flees from us. *We know we have been healed.* Whatever the circumstances or evidence of this world appear to be, this is the word of God.

Seek more faith

And healing *does* include physical healing. Jesus has done it all. There is nothing more for God to do. It is up to us to receive it. We receive it in faith; faith comes from hearing the message, and the message is heard through the word of Christ.

We need to meditate more and more on the word. This increases faith. Also it will bring more revelation on the neglected area of spiritual warfare. Is it surprising that the one who blinded Christians to deliverance ministry for centuries will also, if he is allowed, blind us to the power that there is in Scripture, and in the name of Jesus used against Satan for our own lives? When we don't receive, it can be that there are conditions, to be found in Scripture, that may still have to be met. Sickness is from Satan and there is absolutely nothing in sickness that is glorifying to God. That is clear from reading the word. Nevertheless it is a fact that sickness causes many of us to go deeper, and some of today's disciples get very deep, into the word. They are used to success as Jesus was, and if they don't get it in a particular case, they persist and go deeper into the word. Often they come up with what seem to be the oddest things! But God's foolishness is better than man's wisdom. Bible truths are the key to health.

We have to put our faith only in God, and it helps if our language is right. It is the *manifestation* we seek; we have been healed. We have to put our faith only in God, not in the Scriptures themselves. They are only the way to our faith in God.

God is a sovereign God and true healing comes from Him. He can bring health whether or not we meet His conditions. Nevertheless in His word there *are* conditions. We can be thankful that there are, even when sometimes – seemingly more often than not – he wants more conditions met. God knows our heart even better than we do. It's up to Him. He never said serving Him would be easy.

True healing is by faith in God. It comes from hearing the message which is heard through the word of God. The Bible is the word of God and has to be taken as a whole. We trust that, for those who **know** Jesus, the Scriptures printed here will provide the basis to get more revelation of that word on health. For those who don't know Jesus, our prayer is that they will receive Him as their Saviour and Lord, by repenting of their sin and asking Him to come into their lives. A prayer that they can use is given at the end.

So what do we say to the blind who cannot see? When we have the faith to tell them that they are healed, then we shall tell them. Why not? It is God's word. If we cannot tell them that, then we at least shouldn't be speaking in terms of 'when' you are healed! That is denying God's word. We can tell them Jesus has done it all, and now we have to receive it and meet whatever conditions still need to be met. Wisdom will determine the way a disciple will speak into each situation. We can at least recognise that sickness comes from Satan, watch our tongues and not allow opportunity for the deception that God is anywhere glorified in Satan's work. It is not God's will that any of us spend even one moment without the divine health for which Jesus suffered in order to give to us.

Discernment: God's healing or Satan's?

God, by His word, allows other forms of healing for those who don't have sufficient faith. For example, in Ezekiel 47: 12, it is written that the leaves shall be used for healing. However, let us remember the central warning of this book, that Satan, who brings disease, is quite capable of taking it away when it suits his purpose (2 Cor. 11: 14). God uses Satan. We can use Satan too, but God forbids it (Deut. 18: 10–11).

The growth in both science and the occult in these days makes it more difficult, without God's discernment, to know which 'healing' methods are allowed by God and which are forbidden. What we are seeing is a blurring of the distinction between acceptable medical practices on the one hand and harmful drugs and occult alternative therapies on the other. This serious situation provides an added timely reason for seeking the revelation from these Scriptures. We seek the true healing available in Jesus.

23: Self-help – God's way

Promises, conditions and surrender

Knowing God's promises is an essential first step for any sick Christian who doesn't already have them well written on his heart. In addition we may have to *do* something and see that God's conditions are met, before He will listen to our prayer of faith. *'If I had cherished sin in my heart, the Lord would not have listened.'* (Psalm 66: 18)

We remember too that our bodies and our wills belong to God (Rom. 12: 1; 1 Cor. 6: 19–20). They are not for selfish and sensual pleasure.

We have to make an absolute surrender of our lives to God. In 1 John 3: 21–22 we can read how John kept his **heart** right with God. He obeyed His commands. He did what pleased God.

Our faith or somebody else's?

As we come nearer to God in these ways, we can know that God is bound by His word to answer us. What better way to come into health than the way of faith in God? There can be no better way.

However, for those that don't have that faith, there is provision for us: *'Is any one of you sick? He should call the elders of the church to pray over him and anoint him with oil in the name of the Lord. And the prayer offered in faith will make the sick person well; the Lord will raise him up.'* (James 5: 14–15) *We* have to call the elders. *They* need to have the faith as they pray.

We can believe we receive when we ask (Matt. 7: 7; John 14: 14), but we can also pray in agreement with another believer. '*Again, I tell you that if two of you on earth agree about anything you ask for, it will be done for you by my Father in heaven. For where two or three come together in my name, there I am with them.*' (Matt. 18: 19–20)

We have to *believe* we *are* healed when we pray. Clearly it cannot be a matter of faith if we believe only when we *see* we have recovered. '*So do not throw away your confidence; it will be richly rewarded. You need to persevere so that when you have done the will of God, you will receive what he has promised.*' (Hebrews 10: 35–36) We 'need to persevere'. We have to dare to agree with the word, *not* with the sickness and pain. There is power in the word of God when it is in our heart and when it is spoken from our lips. It changes what we can **see**. When we believe we are receiving healing, healing begins to take place.

Yet apart from all this, God, in His sovereign power can heal even the heathen. But again, what better way than knowing Jesus and walking the way of faith – our *own* faith in God to keep His word?

When you pray believe you receive it

I didn't find it easy to understand faith after many years in Satan's kingdom, relying on feelings, experience and the ways of logic and commonsense.

'*Therefore I tell you, whatever you ask for in prayer, believe that you have received it, and it will be yours.*' (Mark 11: 24)

Faith is believing what God says. It comes as we:

1. Get to know God's character.
2. Get to know His word.
3. Believe the Bible is the infallible word of God.
4. Get the word in our hearts and don't doubt it.

5. Realise that God's word is contrary to our experience and to our natural mind.
6. Understand that God moves in the supernatural and His foolishness is better than man's wisdom.

The doubters soon come along and present a challenge to the faith that has come from the word of God. Whether they are in Satan's kingdom or in God's, it is Satan himself – the ruler of this world – that feeds the unscriptural lie into the mouth of a doubter, and from there into the ear of the believer. It goes something like this:

DOUBTER. You say you are healed, but you don't look healed to me.

BELIEVER. No, but I believe I received my healing. I have God's word for it.

DOUBTER. But how do you feel?

BELIEVER. It's not what I feel that's important. It's what I believe. I believe God. I'm healed.

DOUBTER. But that doesn't make sense.

BELIEVER. That's right. It's not sense. It's faith. Faith in God who said it.

DOUBTER. But that's illogical.

BELIEVER. You're right. It's not logic. It's faith in God.

DOUBTER. Yes, but I don't understand that.

BELIEVER. You're right. I don't either. But I believe it because God said it. The Bible says that God's foolishness is better than man's wisdom. I have found that God is always true to His word. He's saved you from the consequences of your sin, hasn't He? That's because He said He would, if only you would believe. John Wesley preached salvation. Eventually he heard it often enough for his great intellect to be pierced, and he received it himself. His faith came from hearing the message of the word of God. Romans 10: 17. You need to *know*

the healing and health scriptures. *Then* you can
receive the message. Then you will receive the faith.
Then you will be healed. I have the faith now. I
believe I am healed.

A word about symptoms

If symptoms are still in evidence immediately after a
prayer is prayed, is there really any cause for despondency? Indeed is it out of line with Scripture? The
medical doctor can often only treat the symptoms; the
problem remains. How much better to know from God's
word that we are healed, even if we are still showing
symptoms.

Look at it this way. For some conditions we enter
hospital **feeling** well but nevertheless needing to have an
operation. The doctor might tell us we shall feel groggy
for a day or two after the operation, but he assures us
the problem **will** have been dealt with. We trust the
doctor's word, and he goes ahead. After the operation
we do indeed **feel** worse, but now the doctor assures us
that the job has been done. We saw nothing. We understood very little of what the doctor did or how he did it.
Again we believed the doctor's word, and rightly so. Yet
how much more can we believe our God?

With God, the healing is often not received immediately. If it was immediate it would be a miracle. Was
our faith for a miracle or for healing? We are seeing
many miracles in these days; however, when Jesus cursed
the fig tree it was not until the following day that the
disciples saw it had withered. With that faith that comes
from hearing the word of God, and on our guard against
the wiles of Satan, we can prevent Satan stealing the
word and the healing from us. Satan can manifest symptoms **after** the healing is complete, but if we persevere
when we have done the will of God, we 'will receive
what he has promised.' (Hebrews 10: 36)

The danger of the tongue

Even worse perhaps than hearing and knowing God's word and doing nothing, is to know God's word and speak the opposite. God is ever present with us and He hears all that we say; what we speak comes out of our heart. What we speak is very important. We read in Proverbs 18: 21: *'The tongue has the power of life and death and those who love it will eat its fruit.'* In Deuteronomy 30: 19–20 we can read about life and death, and blessings and curses: ' . . . *I have set before you life and death, blessings and curses. Now choose life* . . . ' Jesus is the word made flesh. He came so that we can have life (John 10: 10). We do the choosing. We have to choose life not death. We have to speak the blessing not the curse. We cannot tame our tongues; we need to ask God. James put it this way: ' . . . *but no man can tame the tongue. It is a restless evil full of deadly poison. With the tongue we praise our Lord and Father, and with it we curse men, who have been made in God's likeness. Out of the same mouth come praise and cursing. My brothers, this should not be.'* (James 3: 8–10) We have to guard our tongue and our thoughts. We mustn't, by the words we speak, encourage sickness to stay. We have to renounce negative thoughts however they may come. We have to speak the word of God – life, health and healing, *not* sickness and death.

When the doctor says the cancer is so advanced that death is possible or even, in his view, certain, God's word and our lips can turn around the curse of that lie. Fear comes from hearing and meditating upon the words of Satan. Choose God's word! Choose the blessing not the curse! Choose life! Our relationship with the Father is based upon our knowledge of Jesus and the word. Jesus is the word made flesh. When we *know* what is God's will, we can pray according to God's will.

Unforgiveness

Sin let Satan in. Sin and sickness go together, but we can confess our sin. We can get into the word and keep the belt of truth around our waists to hold all else together (Ephesians 6: 14). However there is one sin that stops healing being received, and where we have to do more than repent and receive our Father's forgiveness. That sin is our own unforgiveness.

As long as unforgiveness remains we cannot be forgiven. Jesus said this: '*And when you stand praying, if you hold anything against anyone, forgive him, so that your Father in heaven may forgive you your sins. But if you do not forgive, neither will your Father who is in heaven forgive your sins.*' (Mark 11: 25–26) Many are healed when they come to the place where they identify unforgiveness, and forgive.

We must forgive ourselves too. Otherwise we remain under condemnation which is from Satan. It makes us run from God rather than to God. We can pray for those under condemnation; we can order condemnation to leave in Jesus' name.

Strife among us

Another of Satan's wiles to mitigate against healing is to encourage strife among us. Because we are made in the image of God it doesn't make sense to love God and yet not love our brother. The absence of love can bring strife. '*For where envying and strife is, there is confusion and every evil work.*' (James 3: 16 AV)

Perfect love leaves little room for strife. Perfect love also drives out fear (1 John 4: 18) – another sin that can stand in the way of our healing. We **fear** what the doctor sees ahead, or what we think the doctor sees ahead; instead we can **love** the truth.

Our fathers' sins and our own

Thus, keys to healing include the tongue, unforgiveness, condemnation, strife and fear. When there are conditions that still have to be met, they may be found in these areas. There is no shortage of Scriptures to remind us of more acts of the sinful nature. Paul told the Galatians, they were obvious: (Gal. 5: 19–21).

It is for us to deal with the author of sin and disease in Jesus' name, and we must not doubt that sin and sickness go together. Maybe it was the sin of our forefathers; nevertheless it *is* sin that causes sickness. '*No-one born of a forbidden marriage nor any of his descendants may enter the assembly of the Lord even down to the tenth generation.*' (Deuteronomy 23: 2) The Bible tells us that we are born sinners. That is the truth; but through deliverance ministry, believers are being cut free in the name of Jesus in these days from past generation curses.

Sin causes sickness

Satan is the author of psychosomatic disorders which are brought about by these sinful acts, and which account, according to doctors, for some seventy per cent or so of the patients coming to them. As we get deeper into the word of God, the Holy Spirit brings more that are relevant to us. We know that God has laid down things that *we* have to do. '*Dear friends, if our hearts do not condemn us, we have confidence before God and receive from him anything we ask, because we obey his commands and do what pleases him.*' (1 John 3:21–22) God created man to have fellowship with Him, and He knows our hearts. John says that our *hearts* have to be right with God, we have to obey his *commands*, and we have to do what *pleases* Him.

The Bible is full of teaching on how our hearts should be in order so that they don't condemn us, on the commands we have to obey, and on what pleases the

Lord. When we draw closer to God by meeting these conditions, we begin to find our requests are being met.

God's word is the beginning and the end of it! Satan can operate only according to God's word. Why don't we? We have the authority; we have free will. Satan has no such freedom and we fall into his hands when we misuse the freedom that we have. The sickness we get is what we allow. Satan isn't allowed by God to put sickness upon us apart from His word and apart from our sin. *We* allow it; *we* let Satan in. *We* have the authority, if he gets in, to drive him out.

Foolish prayers

There is danger in the foolish word spoken against the truth of what God says. We have to watch our prayers too. Prayers have to be from the heart. A prayer for healing seems to be of little use if we don't believe it, and how can we believe it if we are the next minute confessing sickness? Then there is the foolish prayer which is not in God's will anyway! Satan hears these prayers. If we don't pray according to God's will, can we be surprised if it is Satan that answers it? 'Lord, if only you'll get my husband into the Kingdom before I die, I'm ready to bear this sickness.' Satan is so wily, some are tempted to prayers like that, which are based on something really good. However it is not God's will that any dear lady should be sick, nor that she should die. However Satan, the legalist and knowing the word of God inside out, hears that we are prepared to accept sickness and death. He knows prayers like that are not God's will for us. We give him the right to strengthen his position still further on the ground we have given to him. God doesn't need Satan's help to bring husbands into the Kingdom!

Our relationship with Jesus needs to be brought up to date according the revelation we receive. Many of us have prayed these foolish prayers. We need to break the power of the foolish words we have spoken using the authority of our new words spoken in Jesus' name.

In my own situation I prayed the prayer set out by Charles Capps in *Why Tragedy Happens to Christians*. Like the book, the prayer itself covers much useful ground. When thoroughly understood, a prayer something like this can be prayed carefully from the heart:

Father, in the name of Jesus, the entrance of Your Word has brought light to me. Because Your Word has said it, I believe it; and from this hour forth, I will pray my desires. I will rebuke the problem, speak to it, and tell it to be gone!
Father, I repent of all the foolish prayers I have prayed, of all the things I have set into motion which would work against me. With the authority of my words, I break the power of every foolish word which I have spoken, in Jesus' name.
No evil will befall me. Neither shall any plague come nigh my dwelling. You have given Your angels charge over me. They keep me in all my ways. In my pathway is life and there is no death.
I am a doer of the Word of God.
I am blessed in my deeds.
In Jesus' name, I stop every force that has been set in motion by my foolish words.
I ask Your forgiveness and I receive that forgiveness now. I will keep my mouth and speak only that which edifies. I will let no corrupt communication proceed from my mouth in prayer or in speech. I will speak only that which is good for edifying, that it will minister grace to the hearer. I will not grieve the Holy Spirit of God.
Now, Father, in Jesus' name, I proclaim that I am delivered from the powers of darkness. I am standing in the liberty of the Lord Jesus Christ and

walking in victory, for the Greater One dwelleth in me.

In Jesus' name, it is so!*

* From *Why Tragedy Happens to Christians* by Charles Capps Copyright © 1980 Harrison House Publishers, P.O. Box 35035, Tulsa, Oklahoma 74135, U.S.A.

24: The greatest physician

In this section we have seen and emphasised the truth that is most important for our health: Jesus Christ bore our sicknesses and pains in His own body so that we don't have to bear them. We have seen that divine health is our right. It is received in faith in the same way as salvation from the eternal consequences of sin.

We have looked at some of the ways in which a walk with the Lord might need a closer examination to bring it into line with revelation from the word of God and to secure divine health. To be sick and receive healing is not God's best; it is better to live in divine health. However we now look at God's provision for healing.

Jesus – our example

Now we take a look at the gospels and see how Jesus ministered healing. In that light we can better understand what is expected of us. Laying hands on the sick so that they shall recover, and driving out demons in the name of Jesus, is part of His commission to us.

Jesus is the same yesterday, today and forever, and when we lay hands on the sick and drive out demons, Jesus works with us (Mark 16: 20). It seems sensible therefore to look at the descriptions in the gospels of how Jesus did it.

Jesus healed *all* who came to Him (Matthew 8: 16) and He healed *every* kind of disease; there were no hard cases (Matthew 9: 35). Jesus looked for faith. Most of the healing stories speak of faith; He could do little in Galilee. He didn't use any system, method or ritual. One healing was usually very different from the next. Jesus wanted thanks to be given to God (Luke 17: 16). He drove out demons that caused sickness (Matthew 8: 16). In the synagogues, the first thing He did was to teach and preach the gospel (Matthew 9: 35). He met the health needs of the people whenever they came to Him. He didn't want any publicity (Matthew 9: 30). He wasn't put off by circumstances when he saw a need (Luke 14: 1).

Signs and wonders are for today

God has delegated His authority and power to us. Jesus is with us today, so we too can expect signs and wonders. Paul spoke of what Christ accomplished through him in leading the gentiles to obey God. How did he do it? '– by the power of signs and miracles, through the power of the Spirit.' (Romans 15: 19)

We have been given the authority to make disciples, to cast out demons in Jesus' name and to lay hands on the sick so they shall recover. This was given to Paul and to every disciple. In Mark Chapter Sixteen, Jesus said in effect: *you* do it now!

With the power of the Holy Spirit dwelling within us, we are taking over from Jesus the job of making disciples. Paul, and Jesus himself, saw signs and wonders. How can we expect to get by without the power of God seen manifested through us, especially since the Bible provides for it?

Paul had faith in God. Jesus had told us that anyone who had faith in Him would do what He had been doing. Paul did what Jesus had been doing, and it is for *us* to do what Jesus had been doing. Jesus said: ' . . . *anyone who has faith in me will do what I have been doing. He will do even greater things than these. . . . and I will do whatever you ask in my name, so that the Son may bring glory to the Father*' (John 14: 12–13)

Building the church

The last great commission in Mark Sixteen describes the job of the Christian. Fellowships, and Christians within them, will grow and be 'effective and productive' (2 Peter 1: 8) when, from revelation of the word of God it is seen that God's purpose for believers is to make disciples, and that signs and wonders are a necessary and effective way to do it. They shall lay hands on the sick, and they *shall* be healed; in the name of Jesus they *shall* drive out demons. It was through the signs and wonders of believers that many were 'added to their number' in Acts 5: 10–14.

I believe that is God's purpose today. James said we have to be *doers* of the word. He goes further and even seems to be saying to us that we deceive ourselves when we listen to the word and go no further: *'Do not merely listen to the word, and so deceive yourselves. Do what it says.'* (James 1: 22)

God's prescription is Jesus: 'The word made flesh'

What we have is a prescription for all. Jesus healed all those who came to Him. He is the same yesterday, today and forever. He will be with us as we exercise our authority in His name. The most important thing is to know Jesus and get that authority.

The good news is that those who haven't received Jesus Christ into their hearts as Saviour and Lord (John 1: 12) can repent of their sins and be born again with the promise of eternal life. Jesus said: *'I tell you the truth, unless a man is born again, he cannot see the Kingdom of God'* (John 3: 3), and *'Whoever believes in the Son has eternal life, but whoever rejects the Son will not see life for God's wrath remains on him'* (John 3: 36).

For you, Jesus is only a prayer away. He is your Saviour and your Healer. Jesus lives. If you have a faith even the size of a small mustard seed, you will ask Him into your life now. That seed of faith will then grow in a supernatural way, and it is a way that you cannot really yet understand. You will walk with Jesus. Faith in God will come from His supernatural word. Jesus, 'the word made flesh' (John 1: 14), is God's gift to you. The way to health is through faith in Him.

Jesus really is just a prayer away, and a prayer that you can pray is given in Chapter twenty-five.

Confess with your mouth and be healed

Many who already know Jesus have received His word on healing through the Scriptures given in this part of the book. We have made Jesus our Lord. We can receive Him as our Healer too.

Romans 10: 9–10 is an important Scripture for salvation, but since the Greek word *sozo* means 'healed' as well as 'saved' in these verses, we can now, given the revelation from the healing scriptures, confess Jesus as our Healer. My own words went something like this:

> Father, your word says in Romans 10: 10 that it is
> with my heart that I believe and am justified, and
> it is with my mouth that I am saved and healed.
> According to that word I confess with my mouth
> that Jesus is Lord and Jesus is my Healer. I receive
> my healing as I received my salvation, and I walk
> in divine health. Jesus is my Lord and my Healer:
> His mercy endures for ever!

25: Salvation, healing and wholeness: God's will for all

If you do not know Jesus

This book has been addressed mainly to Christians baptised by the Holy Spirit. Matthew (3:11) writes of 'baptism by the Holy Spirit'. This is not a ritual. Jesus received it when he was thirty years old and the dove descended (Mark 1:10). The disciples received it at Pentecost (Acts 2:4). Many have received it all through the ages. My own baptism by the Holy Spirit was on the same day that I was born again. Then followed the baptism in the spirit of my wife, my daughter, and so on. It is there, and when you seek it God has it ready for you (Luke 11:13). I believe the secret is to want every free gift that God has to give. We never understand them until we have them! Then we can't explain them! Open your heart to God. Let the Holy Spirit Himself be your counsellor and bring alive the Bible to you. You have to make the first move! God made you to have fellowship with Him. He gave you free will so that you could choose as you would any relationship. You cannot know Jesus until you stretch out your hand to Him; you can't know what you've been missing until you know Him. Until you do know Him and are baptised by His Holy Spirit many of the things described in this book which come from the Spirit of God will be 'foolishness to you'. That is what the Bible says.

So ask God to help you as you read the truth that follows: (pray from your heart and note the Scriptures carefully)

KNOW that God and Satan are warring in the spiritual dimension.

KNOW that Jesus Christ, the Son of God, has already won the victory by His death on the cross.

KNOW that you too can be in God's spiritual realm with Him.

KNOW the position of the Christian: *'We know that we are children of God, and that the whole world is under the control of Satan'* (1 John 5:19).

KNOW the opportunity that God gives the unbeliever: *'Here I am! I stand at the door and knock. If anyone hears my voice and opens the door, I will go in and eat with him, and he with me'.* (Revelation 3:20).

KNOW *'that if you confess with your mouth "Jesus is Lord", and believe in your heart that God raised him from the dead, you will be saved. For it is with your heart that you believe and are justified, and it is with your mouth that you confess and are saved.'* (Romans 10: 9–10)

KNOW that Satan has helped your unbelief by blinding you to the truth of God's supernatural word.

KNOW that you are body, soul and spirit, and that your spirit will never die but have a place in heaven or in hell when your body dies.

KNOW that the answer is to step out in faith. Your priority is to know Jesus today by asking Him to come into your life. Ask with your heart and He will certainly come in. *'I tell you the truth, anyone who will not receive the Kingdom of God like a little child will never enter it'.* (Mark 10:15).

KNOW that you have sinned: *'for all have sinned and fall short of the glory of God.'* (Romans 3:23)

KNOW that you need to repent and that Jesus said, *'unless you repent you too will all perish'* (Luke 13:3)

KNOW that the Bible says that when you forsake your ways and thoughts and turn to God *'he will freely pardon.'* (Isaiah 55:7)

KNOW that Jesus wants you to turn away from the sin

that is in all men. He wants you to be born again. He
wants you out of Satan's grip and in the Kingdom of
God. Remember you have to 'open the door' to God
and ask Him in. ' . . . *Jesus declared, "I tell you the
truth, unless a man is born again, he cannot see the
Kingdom of God".'* (John 3:3).

KNOW that without the Holy Spirit you do not accept
things that come from the Spirit of God (1 Cor. 2:14).

KNOW that God wants you to be baptised by the Holy
Spirit (Matt. 3:11, John 14:26. Acts 19:6) Remember
you have to ask!

KNOW that when the Holy Spirit comes upon you you
will receive power (Acts 1:8). The spiritual gifts (1
Cor. 12:8–10) can then be received from Him.

The important step for those who are not sure they know Jesus

Perhaps you thought you had to be good in some way
in order to become a Christian. Or perhaps you thought
your christening, confirmation or churchgoing was the
answer. These are Satan's lies and they are *not* the
answer. The answer is to believe in Jesus and ask Him
into your life.

If you want Jesus to come into your life you can pray
this prayer – carefully from your heart. You can also
pray this prayer if you are not sure you have Jesus in
your life. It can be a rededication of your life to Him:

Jesus, I believe you are the Son of God, you died on
the cross bearing the guilt and the penalty of my
sin, and God raised you from the dead.
Jesus, I have sinned by my thoughts, words and
actions. I have cut myself off from God. My own
efforts will not save me.
Jesus, I am sorry for my sins and I repent.
Jesus, I give my life back to you.
Jesus, I ask you to come into my life

– as my saviour to cleanse me
– as my Lord to control me
– as my friend to be with me
Jesus, I will be obedient to you.
Jesus, you never said it would be easy to follow you but I want to bring every part of my life (work, friendships, money, time) under your control.
Jesus, I can now thank you that you *have* come into my life, and I *am* born again.

You are now at the start of a new life. It doesn't matter how old you are or how you *feel*.
1. Read the Bible, and God will speak to you through it.
2. Talk with Jesus as you would with a friend; and pray.
3. Worship in fellowship with others.
4. Witness to others, and tell someone *now* that you are a Christian.

You have taken a big step

Once in the Kingdom of God, when you are ready to receive power just like the first disciples, you can ask God to baptise you by his Holy Spirit. The spiritual gifts can then be received from Him (1 Cor. 12:8–10) and you will be His witness as the first disciples were (Acts 1:8).

If you have difficulty with these prayers or would like help . . .

Some do have difficulty in praying these prayers even when they are printed and in front of them. Satan, the ruler of this world, would seek to stop you saying the prayer. For example, without help, some people are simply unable to say the name of 'Jesus'. You can seek the help of a Christian.

God is true to His word

God is the God of His word. By His word the world was made. He gave us free-will. We only have to take Him at His word. By His word He has many gifts to lavish upon us. His word says that He has for us more than we could ever ask or think.

The author would be pleased to hear from you. His address is: Bury House, Clows Top, Kidderminster, Worcs., DY14 9HX.

If you wish to receive *regular information* about *new books*, please send your name and address to:

London Bible Warehouse
PO Box 123
Basingstoke
Hants RG23 7NL

Name _____

Address _____

_____

_____

_____

I am especially interested in:
☐ Biographies
☐ Fiction
☐ Christian living
☐ Issue related books
☐ Academic books
☐ Bible study aids
☐ Children's books
☐ Music
☐ Other subjects

P.S. If you have ideas for new Christian Books or other products, please write to us too!